ONBOARD SAFETY

D0767077

Gary Ritchie
Master Mariner, BA (Hons), FNI

WITHERBY Seamanship
INTERNATIONAL

Witherby Seamanship International
A Division of Witherby Publishing Group Ltd

4 Dunlop Square, Livingston, Edinburgh, EH54 8SB, Scotland, UK

Tel No: +44(0)1506 463 227 - Fax No: +44(0)1506 468 999
Email: info@emailws.com - Web: www.witherbyseamanship.com

First edition published 2012

ISBN: 978-1-85609-513-6

eBook ISBN: 978-1-85609-514-3

© Witherby Publishing Group Ltd, 2012

British Library Cataloguing in Publication Data
A catalogue record for this book is available from the British Library.

Printed and bound in Great Britain by Bell & Bain Ltd, Glasgow

Published by
Witherby Publishing Group Ltd
4 Dunlop Square, Livingston,
Edinburgh, EH54 8SB,
Scotland, UK

Tel No: +44(0)1506 463 227
Fax No: +44(0)1506 468 999

Email: info@emailws.com
Web: www.witherbys.com

Introduction

Onboard safety is a wide ranging and expansive subject that includes aspects of all operations conducted onboard all ship types. From the simplest one man task to the navigation and manoeuvring of the largest ship in the world, safety is central to the modern shipping industry.

Oil tankers, gas carriers, car carriers, bulk carriers, container vessels and specialised offshore support vessels all have particular aspects of their operation that require certain skills, competence and levels of safety awareness from their crews. However, there are a vast number of onboard operations that are common to all ships, irrespective of their design and purpose, and it is those common aspects of safety that this book highlights.

The purpose of the book is, therefore, to introduce the fundamental aspects of ship operations that can provide a safe working environment for all onboard, from the regulations and guidance that governs and controls safety, to the basic onboard measures that can be used to mitigate risk. These will include sections introducing the shipboard safety organisation, inductions and familiarisations for new crew, safe means of access to and onboard ship, general housekeeping, risk assessments, permit to work systems and specific hazardous activities such as entry into enclosed spaces and mooring operations.

The majority of these key elements of safety are not new. The shipboard safety organisation has existed for many years and risk assessments have always been a central part of onboard safety, although in a less formal manner. Formalised risk assessments, more detailed permit to work systems and more intensive induction and familiarisation processes are all now incorporated into shipping company safety management systems, and it is to these standards that the modern seafarer must adhere.

By summarising the key elements and by providing, where necessary, case studies of related incidents, it is hoped that this book will act as a comprehensive introduction to onboard safety for crews, trainees and shoreside personnel.

Author's Introduction

The introduction to this book states that safety is central to all onboard operations from the 'simplest one man task to the navigation of the largest ship in the world'. The sections within this book therefore stress the importance of safety for routine operations as well as far more complex tasks. The case studies provided to demonstrate the importance of safety focus on the more extreme accidents where there has been significant loss of life, ship casualties or large scale pollution of the environment. However, safety is not just about the more high profile or catastrophic events. Safety is about the individual.

It is important to stress that there is one common factor in all of the case studies presented within this book and there is one common factor that is present on all ship types; people.

The individual is central to all onboard operations and an incident free workplace cannot be achieved without a positive, dedicated and responsible attitude by all personnel onboard and those responsible for the management of the vessel ashore.

Section 2 of this book provides an introduction to the human element in shipping and, in particular, the focus of the International Maritime Organization on the subject. However, it is to be expected that many crew members will be unaware of the principles of the main international governing body. A more practical approach must therefore be adopted onboard ship to ensure that a positive safety culture is nurtured and maintained, with the role of the individual seafarer at the centre.

In order to achieve this level of safety culture, the management at all levels onboard must stress that the individual has a role to play in safety and that the individual has the right to question any person onboard with regard to safety. The individual has the right to stop any task and seek clarification regarding the method of work, the hazards associated with the task and the measures in place to mitigate or control the risks. All personnel must be given the confidence to intervene where they see an unsafe act or hazardous situation. Similarly, crew members must be instructed to report any deficiencies in systems or equipment that might pose a potential hazard to other crew members.

The individual must consider their role within the onboard organisation. They must ensure that they familiarise themselves with the ship, ship equipment and systems, the working environment and the policies, standards and procedures in place onboard. Personnel must follow the standards set by the shipping company and maritime industry and must adhere to all safety barriers, safety controls and safety systems.

All personnel must take responsibility for their own safety and for the safety of those they work alongside. In particular, where less experienced crew members are onboard, more experienced crew should mentor them and provide support with regard to safety. Safety must not be considered a management level concern.

This level of responsibility must extend out with the working role onboard and extend to all aspects of shipboard life. Due to the unusual and contained position that all seafarers find themselves living within, safety overlaps into recreation time as well as on duty periods.

Safety awareness and safety behaviours are critical in all working environments and when conducting any number of routine and non-routine tasks. The individual should therefore be open to new safety tools, consider all safety aspects of the task at hand, take time out for safety, observe the actions of others with safety in mind and always plan tasks taking safety into consideration. Safety is something that must be considered continually and must be second nature to those onboard.

The seafarer works in a challenging and ever changing environment and it is essential that complacency must be avoided. The individual can affect this environment and make it safer.

Author's Note

To illustrate the importance of safety onboard any ship, I have referenced a number of applicable incidents and accidents. The purpose of referencing the failures that have lead to these incidents and accidents is to promote good practice and to strive to avoid any seafarer being injured in a similar manner or under similar circumstances. It has been necessary to summarise the findings from these incidents and accidents and, in doing so, paraphrase the reports from which the information has been obtained. It is not my intention to criticise or apportion blame, rather to highlight the pertinent issues. Any factual errors within these summaries or incorrect apportion of failures is unintentional and every effort has been made to provide accurate summaries to improve safety at sea.

Gary Ritchie
1st February 2012

Acknowledgements

Figure 1.9	Courtesy of AFP/Getty Images	9
Figure 1.11	Courtesy of Getty Images	11
Figure 1.12	Courtesy of USCG	13
Figure 1.13	Courtesy of Marine Nationale/AFP/Getty Images	15
Figure 1.14	Courtesy of JEAN MEUNIER/AFP/Getty Images	17
Figure 2.9	Courtesy of USCG	32
Figure 5.1	Courtesy of IMCA	61
Figure 6.3	Courtesy of MCA	73
Figure 8.4	Courtesy of the British Chamber of Shipping	97
Figures 8.5 and 8.6	Courtesy of Drägerwerk AG & Co. KGoA, Lubeck	97, 98
Figure 8.9	Courtesy of the British Chamber of Shipping	100

Contents

1 Regulations and Guidance

The shipping industry is one of the most stringently regulated industries in the world. However, this framework of regulations, guidance, standards and industry practice is not a new development. Many aspects of the modern shipping industry date back to the nineteenth century and the origins of, arguably the most significant statutory safety legislation, the International Convention for the Safety of Life at Sea (SOLAS), date back to the early part of the twentieth century and the loss of 'RMS Titanic'.

Further significant developments have been introduced over the intervening years, including the International Safety Management (ISM) Code in 1998 and 2002, and the International Ship and Port Facility Security (ISPS) Code in 2004.

Figure 1.1
SOLAS and MARPOL are central to safety

1.1 Shipping Industry Regulatory Framework

The International Maritime Organization (IMO) has been central to the development of the shipping industry's regulatory framework. In addition, a number of other organisations and bodies, such as the Flag State Authorities, Classification Societies and Port State Control, have ensured that the legislation developed and adopted by the IMO is implemented, verified and enforced.

Figure 1.2 shows the overall structure of the regulatory framework and the functions of each body within it.

Figure 1.2
Shipping industry regulatory framework

1.2 International Maritime Organization (IMO)

The IMO was established in 1958 and formally met for the first time in 1959. At this time it was known as the Inter-Governmental Maritime Consultative

Organisation (IMCO), a name which the organisation retained until 1982.

The purpose of the organisation was, and remains today, to act as a central technical body for the facilitation and promotion of international standards in shipping. Included within this broad scope are aspects of maritime safety, prevention and control of marine pollution, safe navigation and maritime security. Since inception, the work of the IMO has seen significant advances in the safety of the ship, the seafarer and the environment and the importance of the organisation is without question.

IMO Mission Statement
Safe, secure and efficient shipping on clean oceans

The IMO is responsible for developing a comprehensive body of conventions and measures to govern all aspects of the shipping industry with the aim of preventing accidents and pollution. The conventions range from standards for ship design, construction and equipment to minimum standards for crew competence, manning and shipboard operations.

Figure 1.3
The IMO aims to reduce environmental and safety incidents in a harsh environment

1.3   IMO Structure

The IMO consists of an assembly, a council and four main committees:

- The Maritime Safety Committee (MSC)

- the Marine Environment Protection Committee (MEPC)

- the Legal Committee

- the Technical Cooperation Committee.

There is also a Facilitation Committee and a number of sub-committees that support the work of the main technical committees.

Figure 1.4
IMO Structure

IMO Assembly

The IMO Assembly is the governing body for the IMO and consists of all the member States. The member States are the international governments of countries with shipping interests and this is the highest level within the organisation. The Assembly is responsible for the overall programme of work for the organisation. The Assembly meets every two years and elects the IMO Council.

IMO Council

The IMO Council is responsible for ensuring that the programme of work agreed by the Assembly is conducted to completion and for overseeing the work of the four main committees. The Council is responsible for submitting any proposals from the committees to the Assembly and for advising the Assembly of any recommendations.

Maritime Safety Committee (MSC)

The Maritime Safety Committee (MSC) consists of representatives from all member States and conducts all work related to navigation and collision avoidance, ship construction, ship equipment, safe manning and cargo operations. In addition, the MSC is responsible for all marine casualty investigations, salvage and search and rescue concerns worldwide.

The MSC is responsible for any matters concerning maritime safety and the safety of all seafarers.

Technical Cooperation Committee

The Technical Cooperation Committee is responsible for conducting any technical research or cooperation projects with other bodies and organisations.

Legal Committee

The Legal Committee is responsible for any legal matters within the scope of the IMO. The Committee was established in the aftermath of the *'Torrey Canyon'* disaster in 1967 to consider the legal implications.

Marine Environment Protection Committee (MEPC)

The Marine Environment Protection Committee (MEPC) is responsible for any matters concerned with the prevention and control of pollution from ships. For example, MEPC is responsible for the adoption and amendment of conventions such as MARPOL and regulations and measures to ensure the enforcement of them.

Figure 1.5
IMO Codes and Conventions apply to all ship types

Codes and Conventions

The development and introduction of SOLAS pre-dates the formation of the IMO. Other conventions, such as those concerned with load lines and prevention of collisions at sea, were also in effect prior to the formation of the IMO.

However, the responsibilities for maintaining, updating and developing appropriate conventions, including those already in circulation, was passed to the IMO at the point it was formally established as the governing body for marine activities.

The formal process for the development of a new convention can vary. However, generally, the initial suggestion is made in one of the four main committees that meet regularly.

If the members of the committee are in agreement with a proposal, it can be formally presented before the IMO Council and, if necessary, the IMO Assembly.

It is the responsibility of the Council or the Assembly to review the proposal and give authorisation for the programme of work to be drafted. Once drafted, the convention will be presented again to the Council and Assembly and will be presented to each of the member States for comments. A formal conference with delegates from the member States will then consider the draft proposal and the comments received, in anticipation of drafting an acceptable convention.

Member States will subsequently be requested to ratify or accept the convention. However, it should be noted that this does not mean that the convention is now legally binding. There is usually a period of grace prior to entry into force of the convention, but only for those member States that have accepted it. A specified number of the member States may have to accept or ratify the convention before it can enter into force.

Acceptance by a member State will place an obligation on that State to implement and enforce the legislation.

Amendments to Legislation

The ongoing relevance of existing legislation is of high importance, so the IMO continually reviews and updates it as necessary.

The process for accepting amendments to existing legislation does not follow the same process as for new legislation. It is based on a 'tacit acceptance' which means that amendments are issued with an entry into force date. Unless objections are received by a specified number of member States prior to this date of enforcement, the amendment is adopted without further discussion.

The 'tacit acceptance' method of adopting amendments to existing conventions has reduced the red tape that would undoubtedly slow down the process if the new legislation process were followed. This method of 'tacit acceptance' is now incorporated into the majority of the IMO conventions, including SOLAS.

1.4   Flag State Authorities

The IMO has no powers to enforce conventions. Enforcement of conventions and penalties for infringements of those conventions is the responsibility of the individual member States for their own vessels.

Enforcement of the applicable legislation and verification of compliance is, therefore, the responsibility of the Flag State Authority as the representative of the member State. For example, vessels registered in the Bahamas must comply with the Bahamas Maritime Authority as the designated Flag State Authority.

The Flag State Authority has a responsibility to:

- Ensure the seaworthiness of registered vessels and ensure that all structures, systems and equipment is maintained in a satisfactory condition. This is verified by regular surveys, inspections and certification requirements

- ensure registered vessels are designed and operated in compliance with all relevant legislation and guidance, including IMO and specific Flag State requirements

- issue certain certificates (certificate of registry, safe manning certificate) to registered vessels. The majority of statutory certification is issued by Classification Societies on behalf of the Flag State Authority

- ensure that minimum manning levels are maintained on registered vessels and that all crew comply with minimum crew competence and training requirements

- ensure that registered vessels are suitably provided with navigation systems, equipment and publications (including charts) to allow a safe navigational watch to be maintained

- investigate incidents and accidents on registered vessels and vessels operating within the Flag State Authority's jurisdiction.

Figure 1.6
The Flag State enforces legislation

1.5 Port State Control

All vessels, when entering defined coastal State waters, place themselves within the direct jurisdiction of the particular coastal State. In the United Kingdom, for example, any vessel entering within 12 miles of the coastline will be subject to the requirements of the Maritime and Coastguard Agency (MCA) as the coastal State. This is more commonly known as the Port State Control (PSC).

PSC has the jurisdiction to ensure that international legislation, such as SOLAS and MARPOL, is being complied with onboard any vessel within these limits.

To fulfil this obligation, every PSC has the authority to conduct summary inspections of any vessel within their jurisdiction, irrespective of the Flag State Authority to which the vessel is registered. These inspections are primarily concerned with ensuring that the vessel, and equipment, is in a state of seaworthiness and that her crew is qualified and competent.

Port State Control can take action and, if required, detain any vessel that is inspected and found to be in a substandard condition or where deficiencies in the crew competence make the vessel unseaworthy.

If an incident occurs within the jurisdiction of a Port State Authority, the PSC can take action against the vessel and its owners. A good example of this type of occurrence is in situations where vessels have run aground, causing oil spills into the environment. This has little impact on the Flag State

Authority, but may have a major impact on the Port State.

It should be noted that the responsibility for ensuring that vessels comply with all international regulations lies with the Flag State Authority to which that vessel is registered. The function of the PSC is not to overrule the Flag State Authority.

1.6   Classification Societies

Classification Societies are independent, non-governmental organisations. Examples of Classification Societies are Lloyd's Register of Shipping, Det Norske Veritas and the American Bureau of Shipping. These bodies develop the technical standards to which all vessels must be designed, constructed and operated, which are published as the Classification Rules.

Classification Societies will inspect a vessel throughout its lifetime to ensure that it is maintained in accordance with these rules and, if in accordance, issue a Certificate of Class. A vessel will continue 'in Class' provided that it is inspected and found in satisfactory condition at regular intervals, which are dictated by the Classification Rules.

Classification Societies can also be delegated as recognised organisations that can act on behalf of Flag State Authorities. In this function, the Classification Societies can be employed to inspect vessels to verify compliance with international and national statutory regulations. It is, therefore, often Classification Societies that will generally inspect vessels for compliance with, for example, SOLAS and issue the appropriate certification, on behalf of the Flag State Authority.

Figure 1.7
Classification Societies verify design and construction standards

This process is generally applied to the issue of a number of certificates, including Cargo Ship Safety Equipment, Cargo Ship Safety Construction, International Loadline, Safety Management Certificate (SMC), International Ship Security (ISS), International Oil Pollution Prevention (IOPP), International Air Pollution Prevention (IAPP) and International Sewage Pollution Prevention (ISPP) certification.

1.7   Key Legislation

1.7.1   *SOLAS*

The International Convention for the Safety of Life at Sea (SOLAS) is probably the most well known piece of maritime legislation. It is central to the work of the IMO and one of the first tasks for the newly established Organization in 1959 was the adoption of a new version of SOLAS.

The convention remains one of the key legislation frameworks for the maritime industry. Continually updated to allow for changes in shipping technology and to regulate new aspects of the industry, SOLAS sets out the operational construction and equipment requirements agreed by the convention.

I	General Provisions
II-1	Construction: Structure, Subdivision and Stability, Machinery and Electrical Installations
II-2	Construction: Fire Protection, Fire Detection and Fire Extinction
III	Life-Saving Appliances
IV	Radio Communications
V	Safety of Navigation
VI	Carriage of Cargoes
VII	Carriage of Dangerous Goods
VIII	Nuclear Ships
IX	Management for the Safe Operation of Ships
X	Safety Measures for High Speed Craft
XI-1	Special Measures to Enhance Maritime Safety
XI-2	Special Measures to Enhance Maritime Security
XII	Additional Safety Measures for Bulk Carriers

Table 1.1
SOLAS contents list

Aim of SOLAS

To promote safety of life at sea by establishing a common agreement for uniform principles and rules

Case Study: 'RMS Titanic'

Built at the Harland and Wolff Shipyard, Belfast, and owned and operated by the White Star Line, the loss of the Royal Mail Ship (RMS) 'Titanic' was the catalyst for the initiation of the International Convention for the Safety of Life at Sea (SOLAS). At the time of her build, the 'RMS Titanic' was the largest passenger vessel in the world and was widely regarded as unsinkable.

The circumstances surrounding the sinking of the vessel and the reasons for such a large loss of life are so well known that only a very basic summary will be provided here. However, the importance of the 'RMS Titanic' in the development of SOLAS and all other legislation since cannot be underestimated.

Incident Summary

Only four days into her maiden voyage from Southampton to New York, the 'RMS Titanic' struck an iceberg off the coast of Newfoundland. The damage to the vessel's hull was such that rapid and sequential flooding of the transverse compartments led to the ship sinking within a matter of hours. The date was 14th April 1912.

The vessel had over 2,200 passengers onboard, but a total lifeboat capacity for only 1,178. Over 1,500 died.

As a result of the 'RMS Titanic' disaster, minimum standards for the provision of lifeboats and other life-saving appliances were put in place through SOLAS. This was the first step toward ensuring minimum standards in all areas of onboard safety and fire protection.

Figure 1.8
SOLAS requires specific lifeboat capacities and capabilities

Case Study: 'Scandinavian Star'

Another incident that was a catalyst for the adoption of more onerous requirements as part of SOLAS, was the major fire onboard the 'Scandinavian Star' in 1990. While the loss of the

'RMS Titanic' had a major impact on the development of minimum life-saving appliance standards and requirements, the fire on the 'Scandinavian Star' (and previous incidents) has had a major impact on the fire protection standards and requirements.

Basic fire safety requirements have always been part of SOLAS and subsequent versions have improved upon the initial requirements. The 'Scandinavian Star' incident provides a good example of how such incidents have affected amendments to the Convention.

Originally named the 'Massalia', the 'Scandinavian Star' was built in 1971. Over the next 19 years the vessel was owned by a number of companies and changed its name several times. Most recently, prior to the incident, the vessel had been operating as a casino cruise ship between the United States and Mexico. Shortly before the incident, the vessel changed from a casino ship operation to a standard passenger ferry route between Norway and Denmark.

Passenger Vessels (International voyages)	*Partially or totally enclosed lifeboats on each side, of such aggregate capacity as will accommodate not less than 50% of the total number of persons onboard. Launching appliances shall be equally distributed on each side of the ship.*
Passenger Vessels (Short International Voyages)	*Partially or totally enclosed lifeboats of such aggregate capacity as will accommodate at least 30% of the total number of persons onboard. The lifeboats shall, as far as practicable, be equally distributed on each side of the ship.*
Cargo Ships	*One or more totally enclosed lifeboats such that the aggregate capacity on each side of the vessel will accommodate the total number of persons onboard or one or more free-fall lifeboats, capable of being free launched over the stern of the vessel, of such aggregate capacity as will accommodate the total number of persons onboard.*

Table 1.2
Summary of SOLAS requirements

Incident Summary

While on passage between Oslo in Norway and Fredrikshavn in Denmark, on April 7th 1990, two fires broke out in the passenger accommodation. Fire spread quickly and was accelerated by the extremely flammable laminate covering that was prevalent in the passenger accommodation bulkheads. Subsequent investigation also revealed that the laminate produced hydrogen cyanide and carbon monoxide when burned and this may have contributed to the loss of life.

Attempts were made to contain the fire by automatically closing the fire doors on the deck (deck 3) that was affected by the initial fires. These attempts failed as the doors could not be closed automatically and the situation was further compounded when the air conditioning system was shut down. It was thought that this action would cut off the supply of oxygen to the fire, but it increased the smoke in the passenger cabins, trapping many of the passengers.

Figure 1.9
'Scandinavian Star', as firefighters attempt to douse the blaze in dock in Lysekil, a day after it was hit by a fire that killed 159 people.

The situation was confused and the Master instructed the crew and passengers to abandon ship. The subsequent investigation found that the crew abandoned ship prior to the evacuation of all the passengers.

Many of the passengers remaining onboard did not hear the alarm and were quickly overcome by the fumes from the laminate furnishings. Those that did escape their cabins were faced with thick noxious smoke that hampered their attempts to locate the emergency exits. 159 people died as a result of the fires, which were subsequently believed to have been deliberately started.

The investigation raised a number of issues relating to onboard competence and methods of evacuation. Many of the crew did not speak English or Norwegian, although the majority of the passengers were Norwegian. They were unfamiliar with the vessel and had not participated in a fire drill onboard.

Some major changes were made to the fire protection requirements in SOLAS as a result of the *'Scandinavian Star'* fire, for both new and existing passenger vessels. The amendments focused on requirements to install automatic sprinkler and smoke detection systems, non-combustible bulkhead materials and improvements to escape and evacuation systems. These included the need for low level lighting to assist escape in smoke-filled conditions.

1.7.2 *MARPOL*

The original purpose of the IMO was to focus on safety at sea and to protect the lives of those working and travelling onboard ships. However, the organisation took up a new challenge in the 1950s and 1960s - pollution.

The design and construction of new supertankers had resulted in much larger quantities of oil being transported by sea. These new supertankers had carrying capacities far in excess of any previous cargo vessel and the loss of the *'Torrey Canyon'*, in 1967, highlighted the problem in a spectacular manner.

Figure 1.10
MARPOL applies to all ships, including tankers

As a result of the disaster, the IMO introduced minimum requirements for all ships to prevent oil pollution and protect the environment. Amended on numerous occasions by MEPC, the International Convention for the Prevention of Pollution from Ships is now more commonly referred to as MARPOL.

The main body of the Regulations details the measures to be in place to prevent pollution from all ship related sources. The following table shows the main annexes to the Convention.

I	Regulations for the Prevention of Pollution by Oil
II	Regulations for the Control of Pollution by Noxious Liquid Substances in Bulk
III	Regulations for the Prevention of Pollution by Harmful Substances Carried by Sea in Packaged Form
IV	Regulations for the Prevention of Pollution by Sewage from Ships
V	Regulations for the Prevention of Pollution by Garbage from Ships
VI	Regulations for the Prevention of Air Pollution from Ships

Table 1.3
Main annexes to MARPOL

Case Study: *'Torrey Canyon'*

The *'Torrey Canyon'* was an oil tanker built in 1959. Originally with a cargo capacity of 60,000 tonnes, the vessel was subsequently enlarged to a new carrying capacity of 120,000 tonnes. The vessel was 297 metres in length with a beam of 38 metres and a draught of over 20 metres.

At the time of the incident, she was owned by the Barracuda Tanker Corporation and was on charter to British Petroleum.

Incident Summary

The incident occurred while the *'Torrey Canyon'* was on passage from Mina Al-Ahmadi, Kuwait, to Milford Haven, UK.

Approaching the South West coast of England on 18th March 1967, the tanker struck Pollard's Rock off Land's End. The coastlines of both England and France were severely affected. Efforts

Figure 1.11
The wrecked tanker 'Torrey Canyon' being broken apart by pounding seas, after she ran aground off Lands End, Cornwall.

were made to salvage the vessel and to disperse the oil, but as this was the first major oil spill of its kind the response was limited and unprepared. In effect, some of the measures taken to try and disperse the oil spill using detergents caused as much damage as the initial oil spill.

The ship broke up and sank within a few days, but the damage to the marine environment had already been done.

The subsequent incident investigation found that the vessel had been navigating using small scale navigation charts, which did not have sufficient detail to adequately portray all the hazards to navigation in the area. The vessel was using the Loran electronic positioning system as its primary

navigation tool and this was not the most accurate system available. Added to these failings, prior to the grounding, the vessel was trying to negotiate an area of high traffic density, which consisted of mainly fishing vessels. Confusion between the bridge team as to what method of steering was being used confused matters further.

As a result of the grounding and the significant environmental damage caused, the IMO introduced a number of preventative measures aimed at reducing the likelihood of future oil tanker incidents and, where such incidents do occur, providing an effective emergency response.

The introduction of MARPOL was the most far reaching of these measures and has, over the years, been updated to not only incorporate measures to prevent oil pollution, but also pollution by chemicals, sewage, garbage and air.

1.7.3   ISM CODE

The International Management Code for the Safe Operation of Ships and for Pollution Prevention (ISM Code) was adopted by the IMO as a direct result of the capsizing of the RoRo 'Herald of Free Enterprise' in 1987.

The loss of the 'Herald of Free Enterprise' highlighted numerous failures in the management system onboard the RoRo, in the management of the company's fleet of vessels and in the link between the onboard and onshore management teams. These failures all contributed to the large loss of life and resulted in the most important new legislation since SOLAS was first introduced.

Aim of the ISM Code

To provide an international standard for the safe management and operation of ships and for pollution prevention

The purpose of the ISM Code was to ensure that the failures that were evident in the case of the *'Herald of Free Enterprise'* and others were not repeated. The Code was, therefore, established to provide a recognised international standard for safe operation. The ISM Code mandates the creation of a Safety Management System (SMS), which in the context of the Code is a structured and documented system clearly stating, and providing guidance on the implementation of, a company's safety and environmental protection policies.

Divided into two parts, the Code requires all shipping companies to:

- Identify all risks that personnel may be exposed to in the safe operation of the vessel. Providing suitable safeguards and mitigation to such risks is essential to comply with the Code

- identify critical operations onboard all company vessels and to provide suitable guidance and procedures to ensure the safety of all those involved in performing them. Critical operations will vary from ship to ship, depending on the type of ship and the tasks that have to be conducted. Some tasks, such as entry into enclosed spaces, mooring and working at height can be considered universal, but the SMS must consider the particular equipment, systems and requirements of each individual ship

- ensure that all foreseeable emergency contingencies are identified and ensure suitable plans are in place to respond. This includes conducting drills and providing training for the vessel's crew

- ensure a Designated Person Ashore (DPA) is identified within the shore-based management. The DPA is to be the primary safety contact for all personnel onboard the vessel(s) and has a key role within the shipping company to ensure effective communication between the ship-based and shore-based management. The DPA must have direct access to the highest level of management within the shipping company

- ensure that any additional support (technical, manning, safety, emergency) is provided to the vessel(s) within the shipping company

- provide a framework for continuous improvement in all aspects of the vessel's safety performance onboard and ashore

- ensure compliance with all mandatory legislation and international and national rules and regulations.

These requirements and the full contents of the Code were introduced and implemented in stages between 1998 and 2002.

To remain compliant with the ISM Code, all shipping companies must provide evidence that the requirements of Part A of the Code are implemented and enforced onboard all company vessels and within the onshore management structure.

1	Objectives and Application
2	Safety and Environmental Protection Policy
3	Company Responsibilities and Authority
4	Designated Person(s)
5	Master's Responsibility and Authority
6	Resources and Personnel
7	Development of Plans for Shipboard Operations
8	Emergency Preparedness
9	Reports and Analysis of Non-Conformities, Accidents and Hazardous Occurrences
10	Maintenance of the Ship and Equipment
11	Documentation
12	Company Verification, Review and Evaluation

Table 1.4
*ISM Code **Part A** Implementation*

The company ashore is, if in compliance, issued with a Document of Compliance (DOC) valid for 5 years, subject to annual verification. In addition, each vessel within the fleet will be issued with a Safety Management Certificate (SMC) valid for 5 years, subject to intermediate verification. These requirements are set out in Part B of the Code.

13	Certification and Periodic Verification
14	Interim Certification
15	Verification
16	Forms of Certificates

Table 1.5
*ISM Code **Part B** Certification & Verification*

Case Study: *'Exxon Valdez'*

The *'Exxon Valdez'* was an oil tanker built in 1986, by the National Steel and Shipbuilding Company in the USA, for the Exxon Shipping Company. The *'Exxon Valdez'* was the sister ship to the *'Exxon Long Beach'*, both of which were designed and built for operation in Alaskan waters.

Figure 1.12
'Exxon Valdez' ran aground on Bligh Reef in Prince William Sound, Alaska, on 24th March 1989, spilling 11 million gallons of crude oil.

The US registered tanker was some 300 metres long, 50 metres in breadth and was capable of being loaded with approximately 1,480,000 barrels of crude oil. The ship was of typical oil tanker construction and had been designed and constructed in accordance with the requirements of the International Convention for the Prevention of Pollution from Ships (1978). The ship had a single hull with 11 cargo tanks and a series of segregated ballast water tanks.

Incident Summary

Prior to the incident, the *'Exxon Valdez'* had completed loading crude oil in Valdez, Alaska. Departing the port in the evening of 23rd March 1989, the vessel commenced her outward bound voyage to Long Beach, under the command of the ship's Captain, with a local Pilot onboard to provide guidance and assistance.

As the vessel cleared the narrower and more hazardous inland stretch of Prince William Sound, the Pilot departed the vessel and the Captain advised the USCG Vessel Traffic Service (VTS) that he was routeing his ship outside of the designated traffic separation zone due to the presence of ice. Shortly after the departure of the Pilot and the communication with the VTS station, the *'Exxon Valdez'* grounded on Bligh Reef, to the West of Bligh Island, at 00:04 hrs on 24th March 1989.

The speed of the vessel at the time of impact was estimated as 12 knots and the impact, in shallow water, caused severe damage to the outer hull. Although unknown at the time of impact, 8 of the 11 cargo tanks and 3 of the segregated ballast tanks were ruptured. The severity of the damage along the entire length of the ship was such that it was estimated that approximately 115,000 barrels of crude oil were spilled within the first 8 hours following the impact. This estimate was made by the ship's crew using the onboard automatic ullage readings. This figure represented a substantial and devastating spill within such an environmentally sensitive location. However, the majority of the crude oil cargo remained onboard and the focus of efforts within the next few days were to ensure that the spill was contained.

Incident Aftermath

The *'Exxon Valdez'* was relatively new at the time of the grounding and had been designed and built to the requirements and specifications of the International Convention for the Prevention of Pollution from Ships. However, the extent of the damage to the hull as a result of the grounding resulted in major changes to the legislative requirements for tankers.

Although the oil spill from the *'Exxon Valdez'* was not, in terms of actual barrels lost, the worst oil spill disaster in maritime history, the effects were substantial and the incident remained the worst oil spill in US waters until the *'Deepwater Horizon'* loss in 2010. However, due to the remote incident site, environmentally sensitive coastline and lack of a suitable response given, the spill from the *'Exxon Valdez'* received intense media and industry scrutiny and led to major changes to Annex I of MARPOL and to the implementation of US specific legislation in the form of the Oil Pollution Act (OPA) 1990.

The US based legislation was implemented in the immediate aftermath of the oil spill and required all oil tankers built for operations between US ports to be designed with double hulls. However, the MARPOL Convention was not revised until 1992, with the amendments coming into force in 1993. These amendments made it a requirement for all new oil tankers (from a specified date) to have double hulls. Further requirements were put in place for an enhanced inspection regime and the eventual phase-out of single hull tankers. This phase-out program was to be accelerated following the loss of the *'Erika'* in 1999.

US Oil Pollution Act (OPA) 1990

The US Oil Pollution Act was implemented to improve the prevention, response and budgetary funding for oil spills in US waters

 A Report to the President by The National Response Team (United States)

The *'Exxon Valdez'* Oil Spill

http://shippingregs.org/7.re

Case Study: *'Erika'*

Figure 1.13
'Erika' broke up on 12th December 1999, in atrocious weather off the west coast of France, around 8:15 am (07:15 GMT).

The *'Erika'* was a single hull product and crude oil tanker, built in Japan in 1975. The 37,283 tonne (deadweight) vessel was 184 metres in length, with a breadth of 28 metres. The vessel was fitted with a total of 9 cargo tanks and had previously been converted, by the addition of dedicated segregated ballast water tanks. The vessel, was in compliance with the MARPOL requirements at the time of building. The vessel was owned by the Tevere Shipping Company and was registered in Malta.

Incident Summary

At the time of the incident, the *'Erika'* was on passage from Dunkirk, France to Livorno, Italy. In Dunkirk, the vessel had loaded a cargo of approximately 30,884 tonnes of heavy oil.

Heavy weather was experienced from Dunkirk onwards, through the English Channel and into the Bay of Biscay, and the vessel proceeded at a reduced speed. It was during the transit of the Bay of Biscay in a period of particularly severe weather that the vessel encountered major problems. The vessel was pounding and pitching heavily and initially started to list to starboard. Investigations revealed that it had been subject to severe structural failure and there were three cracks in the shell plating forward of the No. 2 starboard ballast tank. It was also noted that cargo was leaking from No. 3 centre cargo tank into No. 2 starboard ballast water tank.

Initially, the Master of the *'Erika'* requested assistance, but once he was aware of the damage and felt that he could control the situation, he considered that this assistance was no longer required.

Later, the Master did alter the voyage plan for the vessel and headed for shelter and a possible 'Port of Safe Refuge'. Onboard the ship, efforts were made to keep the vessel stable and upright while protecting the cargo. Cargo was transferred as the vessel proceeded to sheltered waters.

Although the French Maritime Authorities had been aware of the developing situation with the *'Erika'* and were aware of the heavy list and previous requests for assistance, no mention had been made of oil leaking from the vessel until it was approaching the coastline and the proposed Port of Safe Refuge, which was Donges.

As the vessel approached the coastline, the situation worsened. The weather conditions remained severe, the vessel became increasingly difficult to steer and the cracks on the side shell were noted to widen and water ingress was increasing. At this point the Master issued a distress call and requested assistance to rescue his crew from the stricken vessel.

The cracks in the ship's side continued to widen and, as the stresses on the hull became excessive, the bow and stern sections of the ship broke apart. Both sections sank in the hours following the abandonment of the ship. All of the crew were rescued.

The environmental impact of the loss of the *'Erika'* on 12th December 1999 was significant with a large part of the vessel's heavy oil cargo and bunker capacity being lost to the sea. The spill affected a large length of the French coastline.

Incident Aftermath

The oil spill from the *'Exxon Valdez'* in 1989 resulted in major amendments to MARPOL and the introduction of the Oil Pollution Act in the US. Central to both of these legislative initiatives were the proposed phasing out of single hull tankers. The loss of the *'Erika'* led to the acceleration of this phase-out schedule and to restrictions on the carriage of heavy oil cargoes on single hull tankers, based on their carrying capacities.

Permanent commission of enquiry into accidents at sea (CPEM)

Report of the enquiry into the sinking of the *'Erika'*

http://shippingregs.org/8.re

Case Study: *'Herald of Free Enterprise'*

The *'Herald of Free Enterprise'* was a RoRo passenger ferry built in 1980. Owned and operated by Townsend Thoresen, the vessel was 131.9 metres in length, had a breadth of 22.7 metres and a gross registered tonnage of 7,951. The vessel was on a regular route between Zeebrugge and Dover.

The design of the vessel was fairly standard at the time with three vehicle decks, designated G-deck, E-deck and D-deck. G-deck was fully enclosed and extended the length of the vessel. The deck was enclosed at the forward end with double watertight doors and, at the stern, a single watertight door. E-deck was open at the after end and had a single weathertight door at the forward end. D-deck was a suspended vehicle deck above E-deck. The vehicle deck bow and stern doors were hydraulically operated.

Incident Summary

Figure 1.14
A lorry is pulled out of the water by a crane while the 7,951 tonne RoRo British car ferry the 'Herald of Free Enterprise', belonging to Townsend Thoresen, lies on its side off the Belgian port of Zeebrugge, 10th March 1987.

On the evening of 6th March 1987, the *'Herald of Free Enterprise'* departed Zeebrugge with 459 passengers and 80 crew onboard. On departure, it was standard practice for the assistant Bosun to close the bow doors on completion of loading operations. The Chief Officer, who had overseen the loading of freight vehicles, was expected to verify that this had been completed and then go to mooring stations in anticipation of departure.

On this occasion, the assistant Bosun was asleep in his cabin and the Chief Officer did not verify that the doors were closed or that anyone was in position to close them. Departing the

berth, the vessel manoeuvred astern and turned to starboard. The vessel passed the outer breakwater in calm weather conditions with only slight seas and swell. The bow door remained open.

As the vessel started to increase speed, water flooded into the vehicle decks through the open bow door. This flooding was caused as the ship's squat increased (as the speed increased) and as the bow wave height increased to a level above the bow door entrance. Within minutes of passing the outer breakwater the vessel quickly listed and continued to roll over. Due to the shallow water depth, the vessel came to rest, within a mile of the harbour, on her side with half of her structure above sea level.

Despite the vessel's proximity to harbour, the shallow water, light sea conditions and the best efforts of the rescue teams that attended the vessel, 193 people died.

Wreck Commissioner on behalf of the Secretary of State for Transport

'Herald of Free Enterprise' Report

http://shippingregs.org/9.re

Incident Investigation

The initial and immediate findings from the resulting investigation were quite straightforward. The *'Herald of Free Enterprise'* capsized due to the fact that the vessel sailed from Zeebrugge with her inner and outer bow doors open.

The failure of the assistant Bosun to complete his duties and the Chief Officer and the Master to confirm that he had are obvious. However, the full extent of the failings that culminated in the loss of the vessel are more complicated and include aspects of RoRo design, provision of safety equipment, lack of structured procedures and a lack of interface between the onboard and onshore management teams. The contributory factors were both wide ranging and extensive.

- There were significant deficiencies in the structure and competence of the shore management trusted with overseeing the safe operation of the ship and sister ships. Little notice was taken of the opinions or concerns of the Masters within the fleet

- prior to the incident, UK Merchant Shipping Notice M.1188 'Good Ship Management', had been issued. This notice recommended that all shipping companies should designate a person ashore with responsibility for monitoring the technical and safety aspects of the operation of its ships and for providing appropriate shore-based backup. This advice was not followed

- there were rudimentary company standing orders that had been issued by the operator. However, these standing orders did not provide sufficient clear and unambiguous guidance to the ship's crew (and other crews in the fleet) regarding critical operations such as stability conditions,

closing of bow and stern doors and departure from port. This is of particular importance where crew move from vessel to vessel, as they did within this fleet

- although a general instruction was in place onboard the vessel indicating that the loading officer was to 'ensure that the bow and stern doors were secured when leaving port', it did not appear that the procedure was fully complied with

- there were 5 previously recorded incidents where ships within the fleet had proceeded to sea without the bow doors being closed. The company was aware of these incidents, but no information had been provided to the Masters on the other vessels

- the 'Herald of Free Enterprise' was fitted with 'clam' doors. These could not be seen from the bridge in the same way as the standard visor doors. The need for comprehensive standing orders to ensure the bow doors were closed or provide an appropriate monitoring system, such as indicator lights or closed circuit television (CCTV) if considered, were never implemented

- the Masters had previously raised concerns over the lack of indicator lights to show whether the bow and stern doors were open or closed. This had not been given enough consideration by shore management. It is noted that within days of the 'Herald of Free Enterprise' disaster, indicator lights had been fitted on the remaining vessels of the same class

- the deck officers felt under pressure to go to mooring stations as soon as loading was completed. This meant they would leave the car decks before the doors were closed and could not verify that they were secure. No thought had been given to this time pressure and the duties of the officers onboard

- complaints had been forwarded to the company concerning the inability to read the draught marks of the vessels within the fleet. Fictitious entries had been recorded in the logbooks regarding draught and trim and it is quite possible that the vessel was overloaded significantly at departure

- there were often discrepancies in the weights of vehicles loaded on the vessel and it was known that passenger numbers had previously exceeded the maximum allowable levels, as designated by the life-saving appliances provided onboard the vessel. Overloading was a potential problem

- once the vessel had grounded and capsized, emergency lighting did initially come on. However, it went off almost immediately. Self-contained, watertight emergency lighting units were not fitted onboard

- the vessel rested on her side, which effectively turned all internal alleyways into vertical shafts. Emergency and life-saving

equipment within the ship were inadequate to deal with these circumstances and the means of escape on the vessel were severely compromised

- the approved stability book provided for the 'Herald of Free Enterprise' did not provide sufficient stability information for conditions when trimmed substantially. The Master could not, therefore, adequately and accurately determine the stability of the vessel.

Some of these failings were addressed by the implementation of changes to RoRo design, construction and stability criteria.

The remaining failings were addressed by the introduction of the ISM Code by requiring, specifically in this case:

- All critical operations to be identified and procedures put in place to safely complete such operations. Critical operations in the case of the 'Herald of Free Enterprise' would have included loading and unloading (stability criteria), mooring stations and the closure and securing of the bow and stern doors prior to departure from port

- the introduction of a Designated Person Ashore (DPA) responsible for safety onboard the fleet of vessels and with direct access to the highest level of management within the shipping company

- the formation of a structured onshore management team to

provide support to the onboard management team

- the review and analysis of all incidents. In the case of the *'Herald of Free Enterprise'* disaster, the failings of previous incidents would have been highlighted and procedures could have been put in place to avert such a tragedy

- the implementation of formalised feedback from the vessels in the form of Masters' reviews. These written reviews provide the Masters and senior crew with a platform to raise any issues or concerns with management.

Figure 1.15
'Clam' type bow doors

1.7.4 The International Convention on Load Lines (1966)

The International Convention on Load Lines (1966) was introduced

to determine the maximum safe freeboard for a vessel based on damage stability calculations and subdivisions. The requirements of the Load Line Convention were introduced to ensure that cargo ships would not be overloaded and, therefore, sail in an unsafe and unseaworthy condition.

The introduction of the Convention in 1966 was not the first attempt to standardise loading limits. The most well known advances in the area of controlling the loading of vessels are attributed to Samuel Plimsoll.

As trade by sea continued to increase in the nineteenth century, so the number of ships lost at sea also increased. As a direct result of these increasing shipping losses, insurance rates for ships and cargoes also increased, causing concern for all ship owners.

MP Samuel Plimsoll was instrumental in the development and implementation of the Merchant Shipping Act of 1876, which made the requirement for load lines compulsory. The mandatory load line mark required to be displayed on the hull of all applicable vessels was subsequently known as the 'Plimsoll line'.

Load Line Convention - Annex I	
I	General
II	Conditions of Assignment of Freeboard
III	Freeboards
IV	Special Requirements for Ships Assigned Timber Freeboards

Load Line Convention - Annex II	
I	Zones, Areas and Seasonal Periods

Load Line Convention - Annex III	
I	Certificates

Table 1.6
Load Line Convention

To ensure that safe loading limits are not exceeded, the Load Line Convention sets out the conditions of assignment to be followed to specify the minimum freeboards (and therefore maximum draughts) to which the vessel can be loaded. The freeboard assignment is calculated based on a number of considerations:

- The areas of operation of the vessel. The water density and expected seasonal conditions are taken into account to ensure that the minimum freeboard is appropriate for the area. For example, a vessel operating in fresh water at all times will have a different minimum freeboard than an identical vessel operating in the North Atlantic because of the different water densities. Vessels passing from one sea area to another will have to consider how changes in the water density will affect the freeboard

- the general structural strength of the vessel must be sufficient for the assigned minimum freeboards and maximum draughts

- the design and construction of the vessel influences the assignment of freeboard. The position, design,

construction and watertight integrity of all doors, hatches, vents, scuppers and freeing ports will all be considered when assigning the minimum freeboard. The potential for ingress of seawater through any of these openings and maintaining the vessel's watertight integrity are major considerations when determining the minimum freeboards and maximum draughts

- the design of the vessel will be considered with respect to the protection of the vessel's crew. This includes the design of the bow (height and sheer) and decks to reduce seawater and spray from impinging on crew members' safety

- special considerations are allowable concerning the assignment of a minimum freeboard for cargo ships carrying timber deck cargoes. Timber deck cargoes, when carried in a compact stow and subject to certain vessel design criteria, can add protection against the impact of waves and so a reduced minimum freeboard may be assigned. Design criteria relates to the provision of a suitable foc'sle and quarter deck to complete a continuous stow arrangement. In these cases it is considered acceptable that the timber deck cargo can be jettisoned to maintain the integrity of the vessel. This does not apply to 'Timber Winter North Atlantic' freeboards.

On assignment of freeboards, the vessel will be marked. An example of the markings is provided in Figure 1.16. In addition to these freeboard marks, a deck line mark will be put in place (from where the freeboards are measured)

21

along with a load mark (Plimsoll line) corresponding to the maximum summer draught.

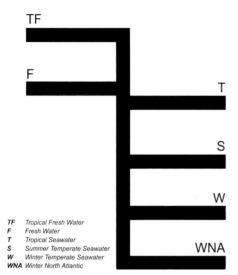

TF

F

T

S

W

WNA

TF   Tropical Fresh Water
F   Fresh Water
T   Tropical Seawater
S   Summer Temperate Seawater
W   Winter Temperate Seawater
WNA Winter North Atlantic

Figure 1.16
Example of freeboard marks

Case Study: 'Cap Blanc'

The 'Cap Blanc' was a RoRo cargo vessel built in 1982. The 38 metre long and 10 metre wide vessel had a gross tonnage of 324 tonnes. The bridge was located forward on a raised foc'sle and cargo was loaded on the exposed after deck either via the stern ramp or by using a shore crane. A powered lift truck was provided onboard the vessel for stowing the cargo and this unit remained onboard the vessel during transits.

At the time of the incident, the vessel was employed on a regular service between Saint-Pierre and a number of ports in Newfoundland.

Incident Summary

Immediately prior to the incident, the 'Cap Blanc' loaded approximately 160 bags (204 tonnes) of salt in Argentia Harbour on Placentia Bay.

Loading was completed on the morning of 1st December 2008 and the vessel departed Argentia Harbour bound for Saint-Pierre at 11:20 hrs. Weather conditions worsened during the morning and were forecast to deteriorate, with winds gusting up to 42 knots later that day.

By 17:20 hrs the 'Cap Blanc' was out of range of the Placentia Bay AIS receiver and the last radio contact with the vessel was received at 20:27 hrs. By 22:39 hrs the lack of contact from the vessel caused concern and a search and rescue response was initiated.

At 23:30 hrs the Canadian Coast Guard vessel 'George R. Pearkes' was mobilised to search for the 'Cap Blanc' and on the morning of 2nd December the Coast Guard Rescue vessel 'W. Jackman', the Royal Mounted Police Vessel 'Murray', a rescue helicopter and a fixed wing reconnaissance aircraft were all dispatched to the assumed last location of the 'Cap Blanc'.

At 10:54 hrs the rescue helicopter located the upturned hull of the missing vessel. The only other debris at the scene was a single empty liferaft.

Crew from the 'Murray' were able to approach the capsized vessel and knock on the hull. Knocking was heard from the inside of the hull.

With the 'George R. Pearkes', 'Murray' and 'W. Jackman' all on scene, the 'Cap Blanc' sunk at 14:08 hrs. No survivors were located.

Bureau d'Enquêtes sur les Événements de Mer (BEAmer) and the Transportation Safety Board (Canada)

Report of the Safety Investigation into the foundering of the *'Cap Blanc'*

http://shippingregs.org/10.re

Incident Investigation

All four crew onboard the *'Cap Blanc'* perished in the incident and no MAYDAY was received. The findings of the investigation, therefore, had no firsthand witness accounts. The findings were based on a number of assumptions made using the weather at the time of the incident, the time and position of the *'Cap Blanc'* at the time of the loss and also from visual evidence from the wreck site.

Underwater searches of the wreck were conducted in the weeks following the loss and three bodies were recovered from within the hull. It was during these searches that video footage of the wreck's position were recorded, which most of the investigation was based upon. Video footage of the interior of the wreck was also recorded.

The video footage showed that the vessel lay in approximately 130 metres of water and was lying on its starboard side.

- The *'Cap Blanc'* was overloaded prior to departure from Argentia Harbour. Photographic evidence showing the vessel in a near

identical loading condition was available to the investigation team and this photograph showed the vessel's freeboard was below the minimum, as recommended under the load line regulations

- the overloading of the *'Cap Blanc'* was completed without any reference to the approved stability booklet provided. No consideration was given to the actual loading condition. This loading condition was closest to the summer load line, but it should be noted that the vessel was operating in winter conditions and so the winter load line should have been the point of reference for maximum loading

- the weather conditions had been deteriorating during the day and at the assumed time of the loss and at the known location, the seas were estimated to be approximately 3 metres. Stability calculations estimated that, in such conditions, a beam sea could pose a potential hazard to the stability of the *'Cap Blanc'*

- the *'Cap Blanc'* was transiting across Placentia Bay with the seas approximately 60° on the bow. However, it is assumed that a loss of steering onboard was responsible for the vessel drifting beam-on to the seas. Such an occurrence had been reported in the previous year and evidence from the video footage also pointed to such an event. The aft bridge exit leading to the engine room was found to be open and the Chief Engineer's body was found in the companion way ladder. It is assumed that he was attempting to restart the generator or manipulate the emergency steering gear valves. In addition, the position of the port rudder and the engine telegraph status were commensurate with a vessel broaching

- the changeover to the emergency steering gear system would be expected to be completed within 5 minutes. To maintain the vessel head to weather during this changeover period, the vessel would normally have been able to use the bow tunnel thrusters. Unfortunately, at the time of the incident, the bow thrusters had been dismantled and were inoperative

- broached beam to the heavy seas and in an overloaded condition, it is assumed that the vessel quickly developed a rolling period synchronised with the swell period. Once synchronised rolling occured, the deck line would quickly be submerged. With the poor stability condition the vessel would, it is assumed, have capsized quickly and rapidly

- had a signal been received from the vessel's Emergency Position Indicating Radio Beacon (EPIRB), the authorities would have realised that there was an emergency situation sooner and may have allowed rescue attempts to be made for the men apparently trapped inside the hull.

As with the majority of accidents, there is no single cause to the capsizing and loss of the 'Cap Blanc'. However, the main contributory factor was the overloading of the vessel, but had the weather conditions been calmer and the assumed loss of steering not occurred, then the vessel would have reached her destination.

The overloading can be attributed to complacency during what was considered to be a routine operation for the vessel.

2   The Human Element

Studies into accidents and incidents at sea have highlighted the fact that human error accounts for a high percentage of shipping casualties.

The emphasis towards safety within the shipping industry has, therefore, changed in recent years and the role of human interactions and with systems has become the main focus of attention in accident and incident prevention.

Figure 2.1
The human/system interaction

Factors affecting the human element include.

- Ship, equipment and system design

- safety management

- safety leadership and safety culture

- safety and the individual

2.1   Regulations and Guidance

Regulations governing shipping have traditionally concentrated on the technical aspects of ship design, construction and operation. However, realisation that the human element accounts for such a significant percentage of all accidents and incidents has created a number of legislative initiatives concerning the human element and the adoption of a safety culture within shipping.

The IMO's International Convention on Standards of Training, Certification and Watchkeeping for Seafarers (STCW) was introduced to ensure a set of consistent minimum training and certification standards. In addition, the ISM Code introduced the requirement for an SMS onboard all ships (see Section 1.7.3).

The introduction, continued maintenance and operation of a structured SMS relies heavily on the human element to meet the goals of ensuring safety of life and the prevention of damage to the environment. These legislative requirements have, therefore, been introduced to augment the technical standards that were initially the focus of safety within the shipping industry.

The further ambitions of the IMO for the inclusion of the human element in all technical standards, such as ship design, are set out in Resolution A.947 'Human Element Vision, Principles and Goals'.

IMO
Resolution A.947 (23)
Human Element Vision,
Principles and Goals

http://shippingregs.org/11.re

While these are not regulatory requirements, the IMO requests that all ship designers, builders and regulatory bodies consider the human element in all aspects of shipping development.

The IMO has issued a number of guidance documents relating to ship design and equipment layout, a selection of which are referenced in Table 2.1.

MSC/ Circ.834	Guidelines for the Engine Room Layout, Design and Arrangement
MSC/ Circ.982	Guidelines on Ergonomic Criteria for Bridge Equipment and Layout
MSC/ Circ.1061	Guidance for the Operational Use of Integrated Bridge Systems
MSC/ Circ.1091	Issues to be Considered when Introducing New Technology On board Ship
MSC-MEPC.7/ Circ.3	Framework for Consideration of Ergonomics and Work Environment

Table 2.1
Guidance on the Human Element

2.2 Ship, Equipment and System Design

The design of any ship, its systems and equipment requires consideration of the environment within which it will be required to operate. The need to design a ship with regard to the impact of external elements and forces, such as wind and sea, poses specific operational and safety challenges. These external elements also affect the health and safety and operational capabilities of the people working and living onboard the vessel. Extremes of temperature, humidity, noise and ship motion can have significant effect on the ability of crews to function efficiently and safely and on the operation of systems and equipment.

2.2.1 Ship Design

Ships are designed to perform a specific function but are primarily employed in carrying cargo from one port to another. In addition, the ship will be designed to comply with specific regulatory rules and regulations with particular regard to construction standards, stability and safety. Economically, the ship will be built with due consideration to long-term financial prosperity for the shipping company.

These primary requirements inevitably lead to a compromise and the human elements regarding interaction between the crew and the ship's systems and the welfare of the crew can often be overlooked. However, failure to consider the human element can lead to an increase in accidents and a reduction in efficiency. By considering these elements at the design stage, shipping companies can potentially reduce the risks of serious incidents.

Ship design with the human element in mind should allow for minimal impact on the working, rest and recreational environments of the crew. Comfort of the crew should include locating the accommodation areas clear of all sources of noise, vibration and extremes of temperature, in an area of the ship where the movement is limited to provide a more comfortable living environment. Suitable recreational areas and space allocated to crew accommodation will help to motivate the crew and will add to a culture of wellbeing and positivity onboard.

The design of working areas should be such that crew are protected while carrying out their everyday activities. Consideration should be given to the access requirements for crew working in all areas onboard and to the safety of personnel while they are carrying out operational and maintenance tasks.

Figure 2.2
Ship design should consider the Human Element

2.2.2 Equipment and System Design

Technological advances in the systems and equipment onboard new-build ships and retro-fitted to older ships have caused considerable changes to the role of the seafarer. On the bridge, manoeuvring and navigational systems have become more automated and systems such as the Electronic Chart Display and Information System (ECDIS) have revolutionised navigation. In the engine room, control systems are of a more complex design and the role of the engineer has, to a certain degree, changed from hands-on operator to programmer.

Increasing emphasis on automation and the provision of more accurate information to the operator can be considered as improvements. However, the role of the individual must still be considered. More automation can lead to more complex controls and the need for equipment-specific training and competence.

Operators must always be aware of the limitations of systems to avoid over-reliance on automation. The best example of this is where a watchkeeper relies on information provided by an Automatic Radar Plotting Aid (ARPA) without visually checking the aspect and bearing of the target.

The increased automation and more complex design of bridge, engine room and cargo control stations, in particular, must consider the human element.

Figure 2.3
Technological advances can improve safety, and increase the information provided to the operator

Bridge design has been considered with regard to the safety of navigation within SOLAS. These requirements broadly require bridges to be designed to ensure that bridge personnel have access to all essential navigational and manoeuvring information and systems status.

The use of standardised, simple controls and displays is of particular importance where multinational crews may be employed onboard a single ship and English may not be their first language. An important factor to be considered in this respect is the role of the marine pilot. A pilot is expected to board a ship at the pilot station and, within a very short period of time, be providing the Master with advice and guidance on berthing a ship that he has not previously been on. Common displays, in particular, can therefore assist in providing unambiguous information to marine pilots and crews.

Figure 2.4
Non-standardised equipment can pose potential problems for crew and pilots

Equipment and systems provided onboard should be purpose-built, appropriate for the intended task and designed to be used onboard a ship, with due regard to the motions expected under normal and emergency conditions. The design of the equipment and systems should be such that the health and safety of the operator and maintenance personnel is maintained. Ergonomics should be considered when positioning the operator and maintenance personnel.

2.3 Safety Management

The ISM Code requirements all ships to have in place a structured SMS. However, it would be a misconception to consider that such a system consists solely of shipboard policies, procedures and instructions. The importance of a well structured, trained and motivated organisation ashore, as well as onboard, cannot be emphasised enough.

2.3.1 Onshore Organisation and Interface

The onboard hierarchy of responsibility has been in place in the merchant navy for centuries and remains fairly consistent, irrespective of ship type. However, the introduction of the ISM Code made the requirement for a clear and defined interface between the onshore shipping management and the ship mandatory.

The nomination of a Designated Person Ashore (DPA) to act as a clear link between all onboard any ship and the highest level of management within any shipping company is a key element of the ISM Code. However, this is only one aspect of the shore to ship interface that is needed to provide adequate support resources for all operational and safety matters and to foster a positive safety culture onboard. Support in technical, operational, personnel and general safety issues should also be provided.

The lack of a clearly defined onshore management structure and a clear interface with the ship can lead to concerns onboard being missed by shore management, with disastrous results. This was highlighted in the incident investigation into the loss of the *'Herald of Free Enterprise'*. Conversely, clear links regarding safety with the shore management can provide the Master and his crew with a more proactive environment within which a positive safety culture can develop.

2.3.2 Safety Management System

The provision of clear policies, standards and procedures relating to operations and safety onboard cannot, on their own, provide a safe working environment. However, the provision of clear and unambiguous procedures is a basis on which a safety culture can be built. For example, an SMS that includes formalised induction, familiarisation and training programmes for new crew will show all personnel joining the ship that safety is important and has been set as a high priority. The lack of such procedures will, however, have a negative effect on new personnel and they will assume that safety is not important on the particular ship and within the particular shipping company.

2.4 Safety Leadership and Safety Culture

Safety leadership and safety culture both rely on personnel taking responsibility for their own safety and for the safety of their fellow crew members.

Figure 2.5
A positive safety culture requires leadership and acceptance by all onboard

2.4.1 Safety Leadership

Safety leadership should not be considered the sole domain of the Master. Effective safety leadership should start from the shore-based management and should motivate the Master and his officers. The Master and his officers are onboard the ship at all times and can, therefore, convey this positive safety message to the ship's crew.

Crew members and officers look to the Master for guidance and direction in all matters and it is imperative that the Master acts in a manner that encourages and supports his crew. He must act as a role model and nurture good practices, safety awareness and a proactive approach to safety. In performing this leadership function, it is important that the Master considers the particular nationalities, cultural differences and personalities of the crew under his command.

John F. Kennedy
"Leadership and learning are indispensable to each other"

Conversely, if the Master or any of his officers conduct themselves in an unsafe manner the message to the crew and all other officers will act as a negative influence. Crew members will start to believe that safety is irrelevant and act accordingly.

Maritime Coastguard Agency

A Practical Guide for Leaders in the Maritime Industry

http://shippingregs.org/12.re

2.4.2 *Safety Culture*

All personnel associated with the ship must work to develop the safety culture, have a commitment to safety, behave in a professional manner and follow good practices. Where such standards become the norm, safety becomes an inherent aspect of all shipboard operations. It is this environment that should be strived towards onboard.

If such a culture can be attained, then it is envisaged that all personnel will follow the company SMS, report unsafe acts or incidents, stop the task if there are any safety concerns, challenge working methods, identify potential hazards and make suggestions to improve safety onboard.

Good communication between all levels of management and the crew is essential in fostering such a working environment where safety has priority.

2.5   Safety and the Individual

Each person onboard a ship should be considered as an important part of the whole crew. Each member has a specific role to fulfil and can contribute both positively and negatively to the safety of the entire ship and crew. A well trained, competent, rested and contented crew member will be beneficial to all aspects of shipboard operations.

2.5.1 *Individual Responsibility*

It must be accepted by all onboard that they have a personal responsibility for safety. Every person must take responsibility for the safety of themselves and other crew members.

The individual must adhere to the shipping company policies, standards and procedures while maintaining a focus on safety at all times.

The attitude towards safety of all personnel is influenced by the leadership of those in management positions and the general safety culture onboard. However, a significant influence is their own attitude and motivation.

2.5.2 *Training*

STCW has set minimum requirements for the training and competence of seafarers. However, these standards cannot detail every ship type, every aspect of shipboard operations and every different type of system and equipment fitted onboard any ship.

The shipping company, therefore, has a responsibility to ensure that mandatory training is conducted and provides ship specific and equipment specific training. Familiarisation training onboard can be used for certain aspects of this training, but formal training must be provided for dedicated equipment and systems.

Failure to provide training to the seafarer in critical systems and equipment can greatly increase the potential for incidents.

Figure 2.6
Personnel must be trained in the use of critical equipment and systems

2.5.3   Manning Levels and Fatigue

It is generally accepted that as manning levels have reduced in recent years, the demands placed on the seafarer have consequently increased. Safety standards, maintenance and watchkeeping practices must still be maintained with fewer crew and the pressure on those onboard has subsequently intensified.

Failure to adequately man a ship can lead to loss of motivation within the crew and a lack of resources can increase the strain on those onboard

and quickly lead to fatigue. Although fatigue is primarily caused by lack of rest, it can also be due to physical conditions such as excessive ship movements, extremes of temperature, noise, poor lighting and living quarters.

Figure 2.7
Ships are now operating with fewer crew

2.5.4   Welfare and Environment

The welfare of multinational crews requires careful consideration. Many ships now have multiple nationalities and cultures onboard with language, behaviours and national and religious cultures that vary considerably. To maintain motivation and a balanced working and living environment, consideration must be given to the welfare of disparate individuals and groups. This should include the provision of good quality accommodation, good quality appropriate food and hygienic conditions.

A healthy, motivated and well cared for crew are more likely to be positive towards their tasks and safety. A de-motivated crew, living and working in poor conditions, will be more likely to disregard safety.

Figure 2.8
A good living environment can have a
positive effect on the safety culture

Case Study: *'Cosco Busan'*

The *'Cosco Busan'* was a 65,131 gross tonnage container ship, originally named *'Hanjin Cairo'*, built in Korea in 2001. The ship had a total carrying capacity of 5,551 TEUs, was 275 metres in length and had a beam of 40 metres. At the time of the incident the ship was registered in Hong Kong and operated by Fleet Management Europe Limited. The ship has since been renamed.

Incident Summary

On 7th November 2007, the *'Cosco Busan'* was on passage from the port of Oakland, California bound for Busan, Korea. A pilot was onboard for the departure from Oakland and for the outward bound passage.

At 07:48 hrs, the ship sailed with a stern tug attached. The visibility at this time was limited and was estimated to be approximately 1000 metres. Initially the ship's speed was set at half ahead with a speed over the ground of approximately 11 knots. The speed was

subsequently increased to full ahead. However, within three minutes of this order, at approximately 08:30 hrs, the ship collided with the protective fender on one of the San Francisco – Oakland Bay Bridge towers.

Figure 2.9
'Cosco Busan', a 900-foot container vessel, collided with one of the towers of the San Francisco Bay Bridge, 7th November 2007

The damage to the *'Cosco Busan'* was extensive and two fuel tanks and a single ballast tank were breached. The resulting spill was estimated at 170 tonnes of fuel oil and had devastating effects on the local environment.

Incident Investigation

The incident investigation into the contact between the *'Cosco Busan'* and the San Francisco – Oakland Bay Bridge was conducted by the National Transportation Safety Board (NTSB). The investigation highlighted a number of errors and failures on the part of the ship's crew and the pilot.

The summary that follows shows there were a number of human element issues evident in this incident:

- Visibility in the period leading up to and at the time of the incident was severely restricted. The pilot did not comply with the local inland navigation requirements with regard to speed and should, given the visibility, have anchored until more favourable conditions allowed the transit under the bridge to be performed safely

- the crew onboard had limited English language skills and there was a lack of effective communication between the Master, his officers and the pilot. Pilot/Master information exchange was, therefore, limited

- the pilot stated, after the incident, that he did not have confidence in the crew's familiarity with the navigation systems and equipment available on the bridge of the 'Cosco Busan'. The ship operator had failed to provide suitable training in the use of navigation systems and equipment and familiarisation with the company's SMS

- the pilot was unfamiliar with the navigation systems and equipment available on the bridge of the ship, particularly the ECDIS, and had concerns regarding the operational status of the radars. Immediately prior to contact with the bridge, the pilot resorted to the use of the ECDIS solely because of his lack of confidence in the radars

- the pilot failed to make use of the resources available to him, including the stern tug, the electronic navigation systems, the ship's lookouts and the services of the local VTS

- it was concluded that the pilot may have been impaired in his use of the ECDIS and other navigation systems and equipment, due to his use of prescription medication

- the Master failed to adequately track the progress of his vessel and did not intervene at any point when the safety of his ship was in question

- the VTS did not alert the pilot when it became apparent that the track of the ship indicated a collision course with the bridge.

National Transportation Safety Board

'Cosco Busan' Accident Report
NTSB/MAR-09/01

http://shippingregs.org/13.re

3 Safety Organisation

The implementation and continued maintenance of a positive safety culture onboard any vessel requires leadership, support and resources from both those onshore and those serving onboard the vessel.

Although the employer is responsible for the safety of all persons onboard the vessel, the immediate responsibility for the ship, its crew and any passengers lies with the vessel's Master. This does not, it should be stressed, negate any responsibility from the individuals onboard. All personnel on the ship, whether marine crew, visitors or passengers, have an obligation and responsibility towards safety.

Figure 3.1
An effective safety organisation is key to providing an accident free environment

An effective safety organisation should include representation from all departments onboard and should have strong and effective links to shore-based management.

Responsibility

Each individual worker is responsible for his own health and safety and that of anyone affected by what he does or fails to do

3.1 Regulations and Guidance

The Merchant Shipping and Fishing Vessels (Health and Safety at Work) Regulations (HASW) define the requirements for the appointment of safety officials, including safety officers and safety representatives, onboard ships registered in the United Kingdom. The Regulations define the duties of the Safety Officer, the process for the election of safety representatives, the process for the formation of a safety committee, the powers of the safety representatives and safety committees and outlines the duties of the shipping company and the vessel Master.

Figure 3.2
The safety organisation should be appropriate for the vessel type

 The Merchant Shipping and Fishing Vessels (Health and Safety at Work) Regulations

http://shippingregs.org/14.re

3.2 Safety Organisation

The HASW Regulations define the minimum components of the safety organisation. However, the actual safety organisation onboard any vessel will depend on the size of the crew and the number of departments. Irrespective of the size of the safety organisation, it is essential that the reporting lines, duties and responsibilities of all personnel are clearly defined.

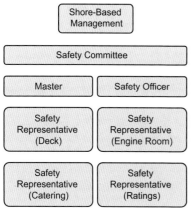

Figure 3.3
An example of a Safety Organisation

The provision of a structured and well-defined safety organisation with clear reporting links to shore-based management should, therefore, include the shore-based personnel responsible for the vessel, the Master, designated Safety Officer, appointed safety representatives and other members of the safety committee.

An example of a safety organisation is shown in Figure 3.3. The number and range of members will depend on the manning levels and departments onboard. (Reference should also be made to the Code of Safe Working Practices for Merchant Seamen (COSWP)).

Safety Organisation

An effective safety organisation will represent all departments on the vessel and have effective links with shore-based management

---

Figure 3.4
Cooperation between all departments and all personnel is required to foster an effective and positive safety culture

3.3 Shore-Based Management

The safety organisation must include representation from shore-based management. Although it is unlikely that shore-based management will be available to participate on a day-to-day basis onboard the vessel, there are a number of key instances where support can be provided. The shipping company can ensure that all personnel nominated to fulfil the role of Safety Officer are provided with adequate specialised training.

In addition, the onshore management should assist the Safety Officer and Master in relation to all reasonable requests for safety information, safety assistance and safety improvements.

Maritime and Coastguard Agency (MCA)

Code of Safe Working Practices for Merchant Seamen (COSWP) Chapter 3

---

http://shippingregs.org/14.re

3.4 The Master

The Master is the primary representative of the shipping company onboard and is responsible for the

---

35

safety of the crew, the vessel and the environment. As such, the effectiveness of the safety organisation onboard any vessel will rely, to a great extent, on the proactive and effective support of the Master. In particular, the Master should encourage the Safety Officer and provide all due assistance and guidance.

The Master must ensure that the Safety Officer and safety representatives are provided with all necessary information, resources and time to allow them to fulfil their respective roles.

The Master should also ensure that any reasonable suggestions, recommendations or concerns raised by the Safety Officer or the safety representatives are considered and, where appropriate, relevant action taken to improve the safety onboard.

3.5 The Safety Officer

The HASW Regulations require a Safety Officer to be appointed onboard any vessel registered in the United Kingdom where there are six or more crew members. The appointed Safety Officer should be someone who has a fundamental knowledge and understanding of safety and must be proactive in all safety related matters. The Safety Officer is the primary contact onboard for all occupational health and safety issues and the person chosen must be approachable, dedicated to the role and should be provided with specific Safety Officer training.

Safety Officer
On every seagoing ship on which 6 or more workers are employed, the Company is required to appoint a Safety Officer

The fundamental duties of the Safety Officer should be to assist all onboard to maintain a high level of safety awareness and to promote a high level of safety culture. However, the remit of the role is such that the Safety Officer will be involved in all aspects of safety on a routine basis and investigate any unsafe occurrences onboard.

The Safety Officer should:

- Promote safe working practices

- assist and advise all crew members in any matter concerning occupational health and safety

- ensure that all safe working practices, guidance and safety related regulations are complied with

- conduct safety inspections of all areas of the ship on a routine basis.

- investigate all potential hazards, dangerous occurrences, accidents and any health and safety related complaints made by any crew member onboard the ship. The Safety Officer should make any recommendations appropriate following any investigation to the Master and should maintain records of all accidents and unsafe or dangerous occurrences that have occurred onboard the ship

- maintain a good working relationship with the designated safety representatives, the Master and any other members of the safety committee in order to foster a culture of openness and proactive cooperation.

Safety Officer
The Safety Officer and any other member of the crew has the right to stop any work where a potential hazard or unsafe practice is observed

Maritime and Coastguard Agency (MCA)

MGN 289 (M+F) Accident Reporting and Investigation

http://shippingregs.org/15.re

3.6 Safety Representatives

The Merchant Shipping and Fishing Vessels (Health and Safety at Work) Regulations require safety representatives to be appointed on every United Kingdom ship that has 6 or more crew members. A minimum of one safety representative should be appointed for ships with between 6 and 15 crew and two safety representatives for ships with over 15 crew. In this case, one safety representative will be appointed for the officers and one for the ratings. In ships with a large crew and several distinct departments, it is common practice for a safety representative to be appointed for each department.

Safety Representatives
On every ship on which 6 or more workers are employed, the Company must make arrangements for the election of Safety Representatives

Figure 3.5
The number of Safety Representatives will be dependent on the size of crew

The safety representatives, unlike the Safety Officer, are nominated and elected by the crew members onboard the ship, with no external influence from the shipping company. The role of the safety representative also differs from that of the Safety Officer in that safety officers have powers and duties, while the safety representatives do not have specific duties. They have obligations to attend safety committee meetings and to represent crew members. However, the safety representative should, as with the Safety Officer, promote and encourage safety onboard with all personnel.

In addition to attending safety committee meetings and representing the crew, the safety representatives may also, with the agreement of the Safety Officer, participate in area inspections and incident investigations and may view the Safety Officer's records. In instances where the safety representative or one of the crew have any concerns with regard to safety, the safety representative can request an inspection, investigation or review of any potential hazards.

As a key representative of the crew in respect of health and safety, it is advisable that all safety representatives are conversant with relevant rules, regulations and guidance and company standards and procedures.

Safety representatives must work closely with the other members of the safety committee and the Safety Officer in particular. It is, therefore, essential that the safety representatives maintain a good working relationship with the Safety Officer and all members of the safety committee.

3.7 Safety Committees and Safety Meetings

Effective safety committees are essential in fostering a high level of communication, coordination and cooperation among all crew members. Onboard any ship, crew members who can see that their concerns are being dealt with in a professional, structured and prompt manner by the members of the safety committee will be encouraged to maintain high safety standards.

Safety Committees

The committee must be chaired by the Master and members will include, as a minimum, the Safety Officer and all elected safety representatives

Figure 3.6
Safety meetings should be attended by all relevant personnel and representatives of all departments

The Safety Officer, Master and safety representatives from all departments should form the core of the safety committee. However, there should be a fine balance between ensuring that all personnel onboard are suitably represented and maintaining a lean and effective safety committee. All crew members can attend, although the use of a safety representative for each department should be encouraged.

The safety committee meetings should be held regularly at intervals of 4-6 weeks. However, this period should be considered on a vessel by vessel basis, taking into account the lengths of tours of duty of the crew and operational considerations.

The subjects to be discussed during the safety committee meeting will depend on the type of vessel, number of crew and operational circumstances of the vessel's location, trading area and working environment. However, as a minimum, the safety committee meeting should include discussions on all previous items raised (and their status), the status of previous safety area inspections and the status of any outstanding actions, details of any incidents or near misses that may have occurred onboard the vessel, any new safety concerns raised by the safety representatives and any other relevant safety information such as fleet safety notices or reviews of incidents from other vessels.

The safety committee meeting minutes should be displayed in a designated place onboard, accessible to all crew members, and a copy should always be provided to the shore-based management.

Figure 3.7
Safety information should be presented clearly

3.8 Safety Officer Area Inspections

Area inspections are an important part of the Safety Officer's role and are a requirement of HASW Regulations.

The appointed Safety Officer is required to inspect each accessible part of the vessel at least every 3 months. It is an accepted standard practice to divide a vessel into 12 separate areas so that with one inspection a week the requirement to inspect all accessible areas of the vessel will be completed in the three month period.

The Safety Officer is required to maintain records of the area

inspections and any recommendations or findings relating to health and safety that were highlighted during the inspection.

Area	Area Inspection
1	*Main Mast and Antenna Masts*
2	*External Accommodation*
3	*Internal Accommodation*
4	*Galley and Food Stores*
5	*Engine Room*
6	*Bow Thruster Room*
7	*Steering Gear Room*
8	*Main Deck*
9	*Forward Holds (1 to 3)*
10	*Aft Holds (4 to 6)*
11	*Foc'sle Stores and Paint Locker*
12	*Aft Stores*

Table 3.1
Example areas for a bulk carrier

Figure 3.8
The areas for safety officer inspections will vary from vessel to vessel

The specific safety hazards to be considered during a safety inspection will depend on the type of vessel, the specific nature of the area being inspected, the operations that are routinely conducted in the area and the personnel who operate and maintain the equipment and systems. However, there are a number of basic health and safety aspects of any area inspection that are common to all areas and to all vessel types.

- The previous safety officer area inspection should be reviewed and any recommendations or findings previously noted should be checked

- housekeeping standards should be maintained in all areas including external and internal decks, the engine room and the galley. Levels of housekeeping and hygiene in all areas, but particularly the galley, should be checked. All temporary and portable equipment should be securely stowed

Figure 3.9
Housekeeping and hygiene standards should be checked

- any chemicals or other hazardous substances stored within the area should be suitably secured and stowed. Information in the form of Material Safety Data Sheets (MSDS) should be available

- means of access to all areas should be free from obstruction and

all emergency exits should be clear and suitably marked. All watertight openings and weathertight openings should be in good order

Figure 3.10
Emergency exits should be clear, well maintained and suitably marked

- potential slips, trips and falls should be considered. In addition to ensuring that housekeeping standards are maintained and that access ways are clear, the Safety Officer should identify any potential hazards such as oil spills, raised (and unmarked) steps or damaged handrails and should check the integrity of structures, such as ladders and stairways

- the integrity of all equipment and the ship's structure should be checked. The Safety Officer is not expected to be an expert in structural engineering, but should be aware of the condition of equipment and any obvious defects

- lighting levels for routine and emergency operations that may be conducted in the area should be reviewed and checked. All areas should be fitted with appropriate lighting

- safety signs and instructions for equipment and previously identified hazards should be adequate. Where specific PPE is required (to operate machinery for example), then suitable signs should be posted. Restricted areas should be clearly identified and marked

- PPE should be available for the activities conducted on a routine basis within the area. For example, hearing protection for engine room and machinery space areas should be available. The Safety Officer should ensure that all such equipment is suitable and sufficient and is well maintained

- safe use of work equipment assessments should be available for any work equipment within the area. Visual checks should be made to ensure that all work equipment is suitably guarded, that safety functions work and that personnel are wearing the appropriate PPE

- working practices within the area should be reviewed if operations are ongoing at the time of the area inspection. Tasks that require a Permit to Work should be suitably controlled and the Safety Officer should check that operational standards are being adhered to and should note any unsafe acts

Figure 3.11
Slip, trip and fall hazards should be identified

- all LSA and fire-fighting equipment should be in place and well maintained. Instructions for the operation of life-saving appliances and fire-fighting equipment should be in place and fire detection systems such as heat and smoke detectors should be operational

- the Safety Officer should consider any improvements that could be made to the design of the area, the equipment available within the area and the working practices being utilised. The opinion and expertise of the personnel who work within the designated area should be considered.

Figure 3.12
Restricted areas should be marked

Figure 3.13
Vessel type will determine the specific considerations when conducting an area inspection

4 Inductions and Familiarisations

An induction is where important safety information is provided to ensure that, in an emergency, everyone onboard knows the appropriate action to take. Familiarisation is a process where personnel onboard are introduced to the working practices and procedures they must follow.

Induction and familiarisations are an integral and essential process within any shipping company and onboard any ship. An SMS depends on competent, well trained, motivated and knowledgeable individuals to operate the vessel in a safe manner. Personnel who are unfamiliar with the vessel, vessel equipment or procedures will not be conducive to a safe working environment and safe working culture.

Incidents such as the fire onboard the 'Scandinavian Star' have highlighted the effects a poorly familiarised crew can have in emergency situations, although this may be an extreme example.

Inductions and familiarisations should not be restricted to marine crew. Apart from passengers there are numerous other personnel who may visit or work onboard different ship types at different times.

Third party contractors may be onboard during port calls, on passage or in dry dock and lay up periods. These personnel may be required to work in hazardous areas onboard and may be expected to work under the same safety standards as the ship's crew. Third party contractors must, therefore, be included in any induction and familiarisation process.

Visitors, particularly in port, should also be considered in the induction process. The areas personnel may visit while onboard may be limited and so the scope and content of the induction should be aimed at such requirements.

4.1 Rules and Regulations

Inductions and familiarisations for marine crew are a requirement of the STCW convention, which sets out minimum standards for all marine crew onboard all ship types, including the specific requirements for crew serving on specialised vessels.

The Convention has been revised and amended a number of times (the most recent being the 2010 Manila Amendments). The amendments provide additional requirements and guidance concerning special training for personnel on tankers, RoRo and RoRo passenger vessels and bulk carriers. It states:

"Seafarers, on being assigned to any ship, should be familiarised with their specific duties and with all ship arrangements, installations, equipment, procedures and ship characteristics that are relevant to their routine or emergency duties"

The requirements of STCW place on the shipping and crewing companies, the responsibility to ensure that all personnel supplied to any vessel are suitably qualified, medically fit and experienced for the intended position they will hold on the ship.

All personnel joining a vessel should carry appropriate, original certificates for their function onboard. The Master must verify that the personnel assigned to his vessel carry the required qualifications and medical certification.

Section A-VI/1 of the Convention states the minimum mandatory requirements for familiarisation and basic safety training and instruction for all marine crew when they arrive on the vessel:

1 *"All crew must be able to communicate effectively with other personnel on board the vessel on safety matters and be able to understand safety information, signs and alarm signals*

2 *All crew must know the necessary actions to be taken in the event of a shipboard emergency, including man overboard, fire or smoke detection or the sounding of the fire or abandon ship alarms and signals*

3 *All crew must be able to identify their muster and embarkation stations and emergency escape routes and be able to locate their muster station*

4 *All crew must be able to locate and don their lifejacket (and survival suit), bearing in mind that different lifejackets may have different donning instructions*

5 *All crew must be aware of the means of raising the alarm (activation points) in the event of a fire or other emergency and have knowledge of the use of and location of portable fire extinguishers*

6 *All crew must have sufficient knowledge to be able to take immediate action upon encountering an accident or other medical emergency before seeking further medical assistance on board*

7 *All crew must have sufficient knowledge to be able to close and open all fire, weathertight and watertight doors fitted on board the vessel".*

4.2 Inductions

Once onboard a vessel, it is the responsibility of the Master to ensure that all personnel are provided with a suitable and sufficient induction and ongoing familiarisation programme that is appropriate for their position on the ship.

The induction process should be conducted as soon as is practical after arriving onboard and should include all basic safety information. The induction should be conducted by someone familiar with the vessel and the vessel's operating procedures and should include a tour of the relevant areas.

Key induction topics include:

- Alarms, muster points and escape routes

- single point authority

- general safety information

- safety tour.

4.2.1 Alarms, Muster Points and Escape Routes

The general alarm, fire alarm, man overboard and abandon ship signals, and any mustering points onboard the vessel or on the quayside during port calls, are the most important information for any induction and should be provided to all personnel, including new crew members, sub-contractors and short-stay visitors.

Figure 4.1
Muster points and lifejacket locations

4.2.2 Single Point Authority

Visitors or personnel joining a vessel for the first time should be provided with a 'single point authority', who will be responsible for assisting them with any safety or operational requirements.

Emergency exits and escape routes, particularly in the areas where the person may be working, and any relevant safety equipment such as fire alarm activation points and fire extinguishers, should be identified.

For example, newly joining deck officers are likely to be advised that their single point authority will be the Chief Officer or Master and engineering officers will be advised to contact the second engineer or Chief Engineer.

However, the provision of a single point authority is also applicable to visitors and subcontractors who may be onboard for only a short period and will need guidance in the working practices, standards and procedures to be followed on the ship.

Subcontractors may have to work in hazardous areas onboard the ship and may have to follow the ship's permit to work system and its related procedures. The single point authority is critical in ensuring that these procedures and systems are adhered to.

4.2.3   *General Safety Information*

General safety information should be explained during the induction process to ensure that new personnel are aware of the key policies, procedures and minimum standards that are in place onboard the vessel.

High level policy statements relating to health, safety and the environment, permit to work systems, entry into enclosed spaces and any other company specific policies should be introduced. This should include reference to the company drug and alcohol abuse policy and smoking policy.

Not all personnel will be required to read and understand all of the company and shipboard SMS. However, a basic introduction should be provided so that personnel are aware of the system and, where relevant, shown how to follow applicable aspects of it. This should include, for example, adherence to the permit to work and entry into enclosed spaces procedures for subcontractors conducting work in tanks onboard the ship.

Specific rules and housekeeping advice (such as waste segregation) should be introduced.

Minimum standards with regard to PPE should be explained to new personnel.

If any individual will be required to work in or transit through areas where power operated watertight doors are located, they should be instructed in the procedures to be used for the safe operation of the doors in all modes of control (remote and local).

All personnel should be made aware of the associated risks of power operated watertight doors, particularly in an emergency when the doors will be on remote (bridge) control.

4.2.4   *Safety Tour*

The specific information and areas that should be covered within a safety induction and tour will depend on the position of the person being inducted. For example, a crew member may have access to the engine room so certain aspects of engine room operations and safety equipment must be explained. However, a third party contractor who will only visit the bridge will not require an extensive tour.

Figure 4.2
Inductions must include a safety tour

The following basic areas should be covered for a general vessel induction for anyone coming onboard:

■   Muster stations and the location of designated lifeboats, including the location of lifejackets, survival suits, liferafts and other life-saving appliances

- fire-fighting appliances in all work and off duty areas should be pointed out. This should include the identification of appropriate fire alarm activation points

- the location of safety plans should be indicated

- escape routes from on and off duty areas, including their allocated cabin

- any restricted areas or hazardous areas, such as (mooring stations)

- designated no smoking areas

- for new crew, and particularly subcontractors, the permit control location and the process for obtaining a permit: This is critical for all ship types and all personnel

- the location of all designated safety notice boards

- area where full PPE must be worn.

All personnel subject to a shipboard induction should be required to sign off, confirming that they have been provided with a suitable induction and that they have understood the requirements that have been explained to them.

4.3   Familiarisation

For personnel sailing with or remaining onboard for an extended period, a more detailed extension of the induction process may be required. This should provide more extensive and broader safety and practical information to support that provided in the initial induction, these include:

- Musters and drills

- safety management system

- shipboard safety organisation

- life-saving and fire-fighting equipment

- ship security.

4.3.1   *Musters and Drills*

Personnel visiting the vessel or attending in port will be advised of their muster stations during the period they are onboard. However, for personnel sailing with the vessel, more extensive familiarisation is required, including attendance and participation in musters, drills and training sessions.

Figure 4.3
Each crew member must participate in at least one abandon ship drill every month.

Personnel should be made aware of the muster lists, their muster station and their duties, if any, that have been assigned.

Each crew member must participate in at least one abandon ship drill and one fire drill every month. The drills must be held within 24 hours of leaving port if more than 25% of the crew have not taken part in drills onboard the ship in the previous month.

Figure 4.4
Each crew member must participate in at least one fire drill every month.

The Merchant Shipping (Musters, Training and Decision Support Systems) Regulations 1999

http://shippingregs.org/16.re

4.3.2 *Safety Management System (SMS)*

The SMS may only be applicable to certain new crew members, although aspects of the system such as company policies and procedures may be applicable to all. Personnel should become familiar with the sections that are relevant to their role onboard, including details of the Designated Person Ashore (DPA) and how to contact them. All shipping companies are required to have a DPA who can be contacted regarding any safety issue. All personnel must have direct access to the DPA.

Personnel should be made aware of the company and shipboard policies on health, safety and the environment. For example, specific requirements regarding smoking policies on oil tankers, gas carriers and vessels that operate within the 500 metre zone of offshore installations should be highlighted.

The rank and responsibilities of the individual crew member will, to a certain extent, determine the sections of the SMS that are applicable to their position onboard. However, there are certain sections, such as those concerning permit to work systems, waste management, reporting of accidents and vessel specific operations, that all personnel must be familiar with.

4.3.3 *Shipboard Safety Organisation*

All personnel must be made aware of the process for raising safety concerns onboard. Safety representatives and the Safety Officer should be identified and all personnel should be made aware of where safety information (including the safety committee meeting minutes) can be obtained.

4.3.4 Life-Saving and Fire-Fighting Equipment

For permanent marine crew and other personnel remaining onboard for an extended period of time, it is likely that they will be a member of the main and backup emergency teams or be included in support teams if they have specific skills and competence (first aiders for example).

Personnel should be familiarised with their specific duties in an emergency, the location and operation of all life-saving and fire-fighting equipment, including liferafts, fixed fire-fighting systems, ventilation flaps and fuel and air stops and the location and operation of all onboard oil pollution prevention equipment.

Figure 4.5
Lifeboats should be included in familiarisation

Figure 4.6
Personnel should be familiarised with the location of liferafts and other life-saving appliances

4.3.5 Ship Security

There has, in recent years, been an increased focus on ship security. Although a dedicated ship Security Officer (SSO) will be onboard, all personnel must be made aware of the security arrangements in place and any duties they may be expected to perform in relation to security, such as gangway watch duties.

4.3.6 Deck Officers – All Vessel Types

There are specific areas of shipboard operations and the SMS that all deck officers, irrespective of the ship type and trading pattern, should be familiarised with:

- The navigational equipment onboard and its limitations

Figure 4.7
Familiarisation with navigational equipment is critical

- the manoeuvring characteristics of the vessel and the limitations of all manoeuvring systems, for example, the effects of windage on large container vessels or large LNG carriers

- changeover procedures for manual and automatic steering and for other positioning and manoeuvring systems, such as dynamic positioning on offshore support vessels and shuttle tankers

- procedures and practical knowledge in the operation of the emergency steering systems

- all sections of the SMS that detail critical operations such as navigation, passage planning, departure and arrival in port, anchoring and other duties to which they are assigned

- the Master's standing orders and routine night orders during passages, port approaches and departures

- all permit to work and associated isolation procedures, tank entry procedures and the systematic approach that is to be followed to ensure that a safe working environment is maintained

- the importance of maintaining the vessel's watertight integrity and the use of the remote (bridge) control panel

- cargo loading procedures, pipeline layouts, tank entry points and dangers associated with the particular cargo type

- ballasting operations and the stability condition of most vessels are under the responsibility of the Chief Officer, assisted by the deck officers. All officers must be familiarised with the ballasting system, stability computer (if fitted) and stability conditions for the vessel at all conditions of loading. Particular hazards associated with the vessel type should be highlighted

- the Chief Officer is generally responsible for the maintenance of the ship's fresh water supply. Knowledge of the tank locations, loading and treatment procedures, pipeline and valve systems and planned maintenance routines should therefore be included

- the mooring equipment onboard, its limitations and snap-back zones

- a deck officer delegated as the ship Safety Officer should be familiarised in his duties on that particular vessel and be provided with a guided tour of the areas covered by the safety area inspections

- a deck officer delegated as the ship Security Officer (SSO) should be familiarised with the ship security assessment, ship security plan and reporting and alert systems onboard

- planned maintenance routines for all deck equipment, including life-saving appliances and fire-fighting equipment

- deck officers delegated as emergency team leaders for musters and other emergency situations must be familiarised with the use and location of emergency equipment, including all portable and fixed systems, shut off valves, emergency stops, fire flaps, lifeboats, liferafts and pollution prevention equipment.

Figure 4.8
Emergency teams should be familiar with all shut-offs and ventilation flaps

4.3.7 Engineer Officers – All Vessel Types

Figure 4.9
During familiarisation engineer officers should concentrate on all machinery systems within the engine room and external systems for which they are responsible

International Maritime Organization

International Ship and Port Facility Security (ISPS) Code

http://shippingregs.org/17.re

There are specific areas of shipboard operations and SMS that all engineering officers and electricians, irrespective of the ship type and trading pattern, should be familiarised with:

- All machinery systems within the engine room and external systems for which the engineers are responsible. This could include refrigeration systems on reefer and container vessels, cargo pipeline and pumping systems on oil tankers and ramps or stern/bow doors on RoRo vessels

- bunkering procedures and systems, including the specific pipelines, valves, tanks and shut-offs

Figure 4.10
Oil spill equipment

- the location and use of all onboard shipboard oil pollution emergency equipment and the procedures to be followed in the event of any spill, either onboard or overside

- procedures and practical knowledge in the operation of the emergency steering systems

- all permit to work and isolation and tank entry procedures and must be aware of the circumstances where such procedures and systems must be followed

- Chief Engineer's standing orders and actions to be taken to comply with them

- all sections of the SMS that detail critical operations such as bunkering, departure from port, arrival in port and engine room watchkeeping

- planned maintenance routines for all engine room equipment and specific deck equipment, including all machinery systems

- for engineering officers and electricians that form the engine control room emergency team, familiarisation with the life-saving and fire-fighting equipment onboard. In particular, the engineers will require knowledge of all fire flaps, ventilation and fuel shut offs, pump stops and the location and use of all emergency fire pumps and the emergency generator.

4.3.8 Catering Crew – All Vessel Types

There are some specific areas where the catering crew should be familiarised:

- Company standards including stock rotation policies, cleaning routines for the galley and storage areas and PPE requirements

- procedures for isolating galley equipment for maintenance

- for catering crew that form the first aid party, familiarisation with all medical facilities and equipment onboard

- all fire-fighting equipment in the galley and adjacent areas, including fixed fire-fighting systems specific to the galley, fire blankets and fuel shut-offs, ventilations stops and fire flaps for galley equipment.

4.3.9 Anchor Handling and Supply Vessels

Figure 4.11
Supply vessel design with forward accommodation

Anchor handling and supply vessels operate in a very different environment to most other vessel types in that they conduct the majority of their operations at sea. Loading and discharging operations might be conducted in harsh environmental conditions and personnel can be exposed to specific dangers. Familiarisation for all new personnel should be focused on safety in this environment:

- Anchor handling and supply vessels are designed to maintain station for long periods of time at offshore locations during loading and discharging operations and are provided with multiple manoeuvring systems, including azimuth thrusters. Extensive familiarisation with the use and limitations of such systems is essential

- all critical operations, including arrival and departures at offshore installations, anchor handling and towing and cargo loading and discharging procedures

- the specific hazards associated with working at offshore sites and during anchor handling and towing operations in adverse weather conditions

- the safe use, maintenance of and hazards associated with anchor handling, towing equipment and systems onboard

- the cargo systems and procedures to be followed for loading, discharging and tank cleaning operations.

In addition, a number of special circumstances can pose specific hazards for this vessel type. Examples include:

- During complex cargo operations offshore where multiple loading and discharging operations may occur simultaneously, the vessel's stability will be constantly changing. Deck officers must, therefore, be familiarised extensively with the loading conditions and limitations of the vessel

- the forward superstructure and low afterdeck design of anchor handling and supply vessels pose particular hazards when loading deck cargoes, particularly pipe cargoes where water entrapment can affect the vessel's stability. Familiarisation for all officers on these effects is essential

Figure 4.12
Cargo operations are very different in an offshore environment

- during anchor handling operations, particularly in deep water locations, anchor handling vessels can be subject to very large external forces (rig chains). All new deck and engineering officers must be familiarised in the dangers associated with such operations.

Figure 4.13
Anchor handling vessel 'Far Sapphire'

4.3.10 Bulk Carriers

Figure 4.14
Bulk carriers carry a variety of cargoes including high density ores, steel, bauxite and cement, or lower density cargoes such as grain and rice

While the safety of bulk carriers has been a focus for many years, bulk carrier losses continue to account for a high percentage of total ship casualties. Bulk carrier design and operational standards have, therefore, been regularly reviewed and specific requirements have been introduced by the IMO.

SOLAS Chapter XII 'Additional Safety Measures for Bulk Carriers' and the International Maritime Solid Bulk Cargoes Code (IMSBC) specifies design and operational requirements for existing and new bulk carriers.

The regulations are designed to ensure safe stowage and shipment by providing information on the dangers of specific cargoes and instructions on the appropriate procedures to be adopted. Standards for regular inspections and specific planned maintenance (hatch covers) are also included.

- Deck officers should be familiarised with the construction of the vessel, with specific focus on the forward cargo holds, bulkheads and loading conditions

- the types of cargo carried have different properties, hazards and the correct loading and unloading procedures

- understanding the trimming of cargoes during loading and the potential that some may have to shift on transit are particularly important topics

- stability is a particularly important subject as correct loading and unloading of the vessel is essential to ensure that the cargo is properly distributed throughout the ship to avoid excessive stress. Deck officers responsible for loading and unloading must be fully aware of all the limitations of the vessel and cargo and ballast tanks

■ both deck and engineering officers must understand the potential effects that a loss of watertight integrity can cause on a bulk carrier. In the forward end integrity loss can quickly lead to flooding and a loss of buoyancy and many bulk carrier losses have been attributed to this

Figure 4.15
Bulk cargoes can pose particular hazards

■ safety systems on bulk carriers are likely to include high level water alarms and water ingress detection systems (WIDS). Officers should be familiar with these systems

■ ballasting and pumping systems are very important on bulk carriers as the safety and stability of a vessel may dependent on them if watertight integrity is compromised, particularly in an emergency situation (collision, grounding, flooding). Officers should be familiar with these systems.

International Maritime Organization

SOLAS Chapter XII - Additional Safety Measures for Bulk Carriers

http://shippingregs.org/18.re

4.3.11 *Container Vessels*

Figure 4.16
Container vessels have particular manoeuvring characteristics

Container ships carry a wide range of container types. The variety of cargoes carried and the handling characteristics of high-sided container vessels create particular familiarisation needs:

■ Deck and engineering officers must be familiar with the different types of containerised units being carried onboard and their maintenance during the voyage, particularly refrigerated units, to avoid damage on passage due to lack of vigilance and care

■ deck officers should be familiar with specific lashing arrangements required and with the hazards associated with improper container stowage. This is of particular importance on container vessels where a large percentage of the cargo is stowed in exposed (deck) locations

- specific stability and loading condition information should be included in the familiarisation process for all deck officers, particularly the Chief Officer

- manoeuvring characteristics on container vessels can be very different to other vessel types. Deck officers must be made aware of the effects that high windage areas and uneven container loading can have on the vessel's handling, motion and reactions.

Figure 4.17
Container vessels can have specialised equipment such as deck cranes

4.3.12 General Cargo Vessels

The use of general cargo vessels has declined as the use of containerised cargoes has developed:

- Deck officers should be familiarised with the hold arrangements and specialised equipment that may be fitted onboard, including deck cranes. The safe use and maintenance of such equipment and arrangements for maintaining hold cleanliness are essential to ensure an efficient loading and discharging operation

- deck officers should be made aware of the procedures and

techniques for the stowage, segregation, securing and protection of non-standardised cargoes.

Figure 4.18
Cargo vessels can be used to carry a diverse range of cargoes

4.3.13 Offshore Support Vessels

Offshore support is a class of vessel that includes those fitted with saturation or air diving systems, remotely operated vehicles (ROVs) or pipelay systems.

The vessels have specialised project crews to maintain and operate these systems. However, marine crew will interact with the project crew and should understand some of the operational issues that arise:

- Deck officers should be familiar with all aspects of diving system operations, including procedures to be followed prior to, during and on recovery of divers. They will always be responsible for the positioning of the vessel, but need to have a high degree of awareness of the impact of manoeuvring on divers in the water

Figure 4.19
Offshore support vessels can have sophisticated systems that are essential to the vessel's work

- deck officers should be familiarised with the procedures for the launch, recovery and in-water operations for ROV systems

- pipelay operations require a high degree of positioning accuracy to along a specific pre-determined track. Deck officers will therefore require to be familiarised with the allowable positioning margins and the procedures for pipelay and abandonment operations

- during pipelay deployment operations, particularly in deep water locations, the weight of pipe and tension being employed to deploy the pipe can create considerable forces acting on the vessel. Deck officers must be familiarised with the associated risks and the effects that external forces can have on the positioning of the vessel

Figure 4.20
Deck officers can be required to act as helicopter landing officers on offshore support vessels

- engineering officers may be involved in maintenance and repairs on dive systems, ROV handling systems and pipelay deployment systems. Familiarisation with the routine maintenance, use and operation of these systems should, therefore, be considered.

4.3.14 *Oil Tankers, Product, Gas and Chemical Carriers*

Groundings, collisions or fire onboard any of these vessel types can have significant and devastating effects on the marine environment and the volatility of the cargoes can seriously hamper any means of escape for the crew. Familiarisation must, therefore, concentrate on maintaining the vessel's integrity.

- Deck and engineering officers must be familiar with the cargo loading, discharging, tank cleaning and inert gas systems onboard

- deck and engineering officers must be familiarised with all the hazards associated with the particular cargoes carried onboard and the safety systems fitted

Figure 4.21
Liquid cargoes in bulk require special attention

- deck and engineering officers must be familiarised with all sections of the SMS relating to procedures and safety precautions to be followed during all loading, discharging, tank cleaning and gas-freeing operations

- deck officers must be familiarised with any mandatory emergency towing arrangements onboard and the procedures and hazards associated with deploying and connecting such arrangements

- deck officers in charge of a navigational watch should be familiarised with any specific mandatory reporting schemes on the vessel's normal routes.

Figure 4.22
Tankers are subject to specific mandatory reporting requirements

4.3.15 RoRo and Passenger Vessels

RoRo vessels operate on strict schedules and can complete multiple loading, discharges and transits within a 24 hour period. Therefore, it is essential that all personnel onboard, and particularly the deck officers, are familiar with the stability, watertight integrity and departure procedures.

- Deck officers must be familiarised with loading conditions for the vessel, with particular attention paid to the maximum loading conditions

- deck officers are responsible for the loading and discharging of RoRo vessels and are, therefore, responsible for ensuring that the stern and/or bow doors and internal watertight and weathertight doors are all closed prior to departure from port. The deck officers must be familiar with the SMS procedures and checklists

Figure 4.23
RoRo vessels have particular stability considerations

- deck officers in charge of a navigational watch will be responsible for ensuring that the watertight integrity of the vessel is confirmed prior to departure. They must, therefore, be familiar with the SMS procedures for confirming with the loading officer and be familiar with the indicators fitted showing such status on the bridge

- the deck and engineering officers will be responsible for the safe evacuation of passengers in the event of an emergency and must, therefore, be familiar with all passenger evacuation systems fitted onboard and be conversant with crowd control management.

4.3.16 *Standby Vessels*

Standby vessels, or emergency response and rescue vessels (ERRV), maintain station at offshore installations and, in the event of an emergency, provide assistance and a safe haven.

The equipment and systems onboard a standby vessel have two main functions; maintaining position in potentially adverse weather conditions and rescuing personnel from survival craft (lifeboats, liferafts) and the water. Personnel on these vessels must, therefore, be familiarised, trained and drilled in the use of all rescue systems.

Figure 4.24
Standby vessels are fitted with specialised rescue equipment

- Deck officers will be required to navigate and manoeuvre in close proximity to offshore installations and the associated subsea and surface infrastructures. They should, therefore, be familiarised with the location, manoeuvring characteristics of their vessel and the dangers associated with such close proximity operations

- deck officers will be required to coordinate rescue operations in the event of an emergency at the offshore installation. It is, therefore, important that they are fully familiarised with the installation's emergency plans and escape routes

■ personnel will be required to be familiarised with all onboard rescue systems such as Dacon scoops, rescue boats and rescue baskets.

Figure 4.25
Standby vessels are usually purpose-built and can have complex systems and equipment

5 Safe Access and Safe Movement

Safety of personnel boarding or leaving the vessel is a primary concern, but it should always be remembered that the gangway or accommodation ladder (means of access) will often be the first contact new personnel or visitors will have with the vessel. The first impression that a well-prepared and safe gangway or accommodation ladder can create should set the standard for the safety culture to be expected onboard.

Figure 5.1
A well-rigged gangway or accommodation ladder helps promote a safety culture onboard

Conversely, a poorly maintained and unsafe means of access will provide a poor initial impression to anyone attending the vessel.

Once onboard, safe access and safe movement for visitors must be provided and safe access and movement to all areas where crew members may be expected to work and transit, must be provided.

5.1 Regulations and Guidance

There are specific regulations and guidance in place to ensure the provision of a suitable gangway or accommodation ladder. For UK registered vessels and vessels operating within the jurisdiction of the MCA, the Merchant Shipping (Means of Access) Regulations apply. Guidance is also provided in the Code of Safe Working Practices for Merchant Seamen (COSWP) Chapter 6.

The Merchant Shipping (Means of Access) Regulations

http://shippingregs.org/19.re

The Merchant Shipping (Means of Access) Regulations require the Master and the employer to provide a safe means of access to the vessel.

The requirement to provide a safe means of access is not restricted to the standard ship to shore gangway or accommodation ladder, but includes any means of access whether from the ship to shore or from the ship to another ship or barge moored alongside and for embarkation and disembarkation of pilots.

Merchant Shipping (Means of Access) Regulations
The employer and Master shall ensure that safe means of access is provided and maintained to any place on the ship to which a person may be expected to go

 The Merchant Shipping (Safe Movement on Board Ship) Regulations

http://shippingregs.org/20.re

Safe movement should be considered for all areas onboard, such as access to change navigation lights on a mast, access to a hold to conduct hold cleaning operations and access to inspect the condition of a fuel tank. Particular consideration should also be given to the provision of safe access and egress from enclosed spaces.

Figure 5.2
Designated safe walkways for visitors can improve safety

The provision of safe movement onboard ship also places on the employer and the Master the responsibility for ensuring that personnel are not allowed to enter hazardous areas without authorisation.

Merchant Shipping (Safe Movement on Board Ship) Regulations
The employer and Master shall ensure that all deck surfaces used for transit about the ship, and all passageways, walkways and stairs, are properly maintained and kept free from materials or substances liable to cause a person to slip or fall

5.2　Safe Access

The Merchant Shipping (Means of Access) Regulations require all vessels of a certain length to be provided with a gangway or accommodation ladder.

An accommodation ladder will usually be a fixed installation with a turntable at the upper end. This allows it to be rotated for deployment onto the quay. A gangway is generally a portable set of stairs that can be fixed to various parts of the vessel, depending on the freeboard, and is fixed at an angle of ninety degrees to the ship's side.

Means of Access requirements
All vessels of 30 metres or more in length must be provided with a suitable gangway appropriate to the freeboards to be expected for the vessel in the varying loaded conditions which will be expected
All vessels of 120 metres or more in length must be provided with an accommodation ladder appropriate to the freeboards to be expected for the vessel in the varying loaded conditions which will be expected

The means of access must be positioned promptly and remain in place while the vessel is secured, be properly rigged and secured and be adjusted from time to time as environmental conditions dictate. The safety net should provide protection at both the upper and lower extremities of the access way.

Although accommodation ladders are generally fixed installations and gangways are portable, the safety and operational considerations for both are similar:

Figure 5.3
Accommodation ladder safety nets should cover all areas where a person may potentially fall

■ Accommodation ladders and gangways must be designed and constructed for the intended purpose. The maximum angle of use and the maximum safe loading should be clearly marked on the

unit to ensure that it is used in as safe a manner as is possible

■ the means of access must be put in place as soon as is practical after arrival and no persons should attempt to board the vessel until the accommodation ladder or gangway and associated equipment is fully rigged and in place. The means of access and all equipment should remain in place until immediately before departure

■ for all loading conditions and freeboards, the angle of ascent of the accommodation ladder or gangway should be no greater than fifty five degrees to the horizontal

■ consideration should be given to activities or obstructions on the quayside that may affect the integrity of the accommodation ladder or gangway. For example, shore gantry crane tracks or quayside mooring bollards may not initially be a hazard, but changes to operations on the quay or the draught of the vessel may alter the situation

■ during port stays, the accomodation ladder or gangway should be tended regularly to ensure the tidal conditions or changes in draught and trim do not alter the integrity of the means of access. Tidal levels for the intended port stay should be provided to personnel designated to tend the accommodation ladder or gangway

■ any platforms fitted to an accommodation ladder, such as the turntable at the upper end, should provide a horizontal and stable platform between the ladder and the deck of the vessel or quayside, as appropriate

- suitable handrails should be fitted along the entire length and around all platforms on accommodation ladders and gangways. The access point at the lower end of the accommodation ladder or gangway should be on the outer side (clear of the side of the ship) to afford greater protection while boarding

Figure 5.4
Steps must provide a stable platform and traction

- treads on the accommodation ladder or gangway steps should provide an anti-slip surface. In some cases, anti-slip treads can be fitted to the surface of the steps to provide extra traction. The treads should be suitable for all the anticipated angles of the accommodation ladder or gangway for the expected range of normal freeboards

- environmental conditions may cause additional hazards that should be considered when using an accommodation ladder or a gangway. Ice, snow or any spillages in the vicinity or on the

accommodation ladder or gangway should be cleaned up immediately

- the upper and lower access areas and the entire length of the accommodation ladder or gangway must be suitably lit to provide safe access during the hours of darkness

- a suitable safety net must be rigged to provide protection at all points on the accommodation ladder or gangway including upper and lower access points

- suitable safety and rescue equipment should be located at the accommodation ladder or gangway, including a lifebuoy with self-activating light and buoyant safety line.

Figure 5.5
The accommodation ladder or gangway is generally the first point of contact that any personnel joining or visiting will have with the vessel. It is most likely that security will be tending the access point, but it is still essential that instructions are posted regarding where to report on arrival

5.3 Safe Movement

- Adequate and appropriate lighting levels must be provided in all areas where personnel may be expected to work or transit. This should include all walkways, stairways, ladders, cargo holds, machinery spaces, stores and workshops

- all transit areas should be kept clear and unobstructed. Loose equipment, stores and other items should be stowed as soon as possible to avoid the potential for slip, trip and fall incidents

- all walkways, stairways, engine room plates and ladders should be kept well maintained and any spillages that can cause a potential slip hazard should be quickly and adequately cleaned up or treated

- access to areas where work is ongoing or where there are potential hazards should be restricted. Personnel, such as visitors, should therefore only have access to specific areas

- any openings where a person may fall should be fitted with suitable guard rails

- emergency exits and escape routes should be marked in accordance with SOLAS requirements and should be kept clear and unobstructed at all times.

Maritime and Coastguard Agency

Code of Safe Working Practices for Merchant Seamen (COSWP) Chapter 6 – Means of Access and Safe Movement

http://shippingregs.org/14.re

The content of these regulations and the guidance provided should be considered good working practice for any vessel.

Figure 5.6
Restrict access to certain areas

5.4   Walkways and Working Decks

Walkways and working decks vary from ship to ship and from ship type to ship type. They will generally be constructed from similar materials, including flat steel, open grating, chequered plate and timber.

The main hazard will be slips, trips and falls and so the anti-slip properties of the surfaces are an important consideration, particularly in areas that may be exposed to wet conditions on deck or where there is the potential for spill hazards.

Where surfaces are made from flat steel, for example, additional precautions, such as the use of anti-slip paint and deck tiles, may be needed. Treatment of deck areas with anti-slip paints and the use of deck tiles can increase the traction on walkways. Pipe and cable bridges can be used to remove exposed trip hazards posed by pipe work and temporary and permanent cabling. Pipe and cable bridges should be painted a contrasting colour to the walkways.

Figure 5.7
Walkways should be free of obstructions and slip hazards

5.5   Stairways

The responsibility for ensuring that the slope angles, construction and provision of handrails is adequate will be with the shipyard and the Classification Society.

However, marine crew should be aware of the additional hazards associated with external and internal stairways.

Injuries can easily be sustained when stepping from one level to another and the chance of falling is increased significantly. It is, therefore, important to ensure that stairways are marked appropriately, fitted with adequate anti-slip surfaces, are well maintained to reduce slip, trip and fall hazards and are unobstructed.

Painting, or using colour coded nosings, to identify and highlight the different levels on a stairway can help to reduce the potential risks. Although the external stair tread surfaces will generally be constructed with an anti-slip surface (Figure 5.8), additional anti-slip properties can be provided by also installing anti-slip nosing treads onto these surfaces (Figure 5.10).

Figure 5.8
External stair treads designed with anti-slip properties

For internal stairways, mats or carpeting should not be placed at the upper or lower landings, unless they are fixed in place.

EN ISO 14122-1: Safety of Machinery – Permanent Means of Access to Machinery – Part 1

Stair (definition) - fixed means of access with an angle of pitch from more than 20° up to 45°, whose horizontal elements are steps

Figure 5.9
Stairway with additional anti-slip treads

Figure 5.10
Stairway with additional anti-slip treads

5.6 Vertical Ladders

Vertical ladders can pose considerable potential slip or fall hazards.

They should be of good construction for the intended use and be adequately

secured in place. Routine planned maintenance and inspections should be in place to check and repair any defects and to ensure the integrity of the structure and attachments.

Backscratchers are generally installed to provide a protective cage. However, other means can be provided, such as guided fall arrestor systems with the user wearing a safety harness clipped onto a fixed vertical rail on the ladder.

Suitable handrails, handholds and platforms should be provided to allow access onto and egress from all vertical ladders.

Anti-slip treads can be fitted to vertical ladder square bar or rounded bar rungs, to provide a more stable surface and reduce the potential for slips.

Figure 5.11
Vertical ladders should be fitted with fall protection

Deck levels should be clearly marked with a contrasting colour to the deck to signify the access point and any raised lips should similarly be highlighted.

Figure 5.12
Fall device fitted to a vertical ladder

EN ISO 14122-1: Safety of Machinery – Permanent Means of Access to Machinery – Part 4

The ladder shall be fitted with a fall protection device when the height of the ladder flight is more than 3000 mm

The ladder shall be fitted with a fall protection device when the height of the ladder is 3000 mm or less, but at the departure area there is the risk of falling an additional distance

Access to a vertical ladder, at the upper levels, should be restricted by a gate, drop down safety bar or safety chain to ensure that personnel will have to physically remove the barrier before stepping onto the vertical ladder.

5.7 Emergency Escapes

Chapter II-2 of SOLAS and Chapter 13 of the Fire Safety Systems (FSS) Code

specify the requirements to be in place for the provision of a means of escape from all spaces.

SOLAS: Chapter II-2 – Construction: Fire Protection, Fire Detection and Fire Extinction, Regulation 13 Means of Escape

Unless expressly provided otherwise in this regulation, at least two widely separated and ready means of escape shall be provided from all spaces or groups of spaces

Emergency escapes should be marked in accordance with SOLAS and the FSS Code requirements and should be maintained in a clear and unobstructed state.

Maintenance of emergency escapes should be included in the onboard planned maintenance schedule and operational/security requirements should never impinge on maintaining the emergency escapes in a state of constant readiness.

Figure 5.13
Emergency exits must be kept clear and unobstructed

5.8 Good Housekeeping and Working Practices

The provision of stable, well maintained and well constructed access ways must also be augmented by good onboard working and housekeeping practices. By ensuring good practices are followed onboard and that any breaches of good practices and housekeeping are resolved in a timely and efficient manner, the potential for slip, trip and fall incidents can be significantly reduced.

Steps to Reduce Slips, Trips and Falls	
Integrity	*Regular inspections and planned maintenance should be conducted to verify the condition of all structures and fall protection arrangements and to rectify any defects.*
Surfaces	*Surfaces of all access ways, stairways and ladders should be suitable for the use they are intended. Additional treads and anti-slip surfaces should be fitted as necessary and the use of mats and carpets in certain areas (top of stairways) should be avoided.*
Marking	*Changes in levels, access points, emergency exits and any recognised trip hazards should be clearly marked.*
Lighting	*Lighting should be suitable for the area and should be sufficient to ensure that potential hazards are visible.*
Restrict Access	*Restricted areas should be clearly marked to restrict access to hazardous areas, for example, where tank lids have been removed for tank entry purposes or where cargo or stores hatches may be open.*
Housekeeping	*Walkways and access ways must be kept free of obstructions, loose and unsecured equipment should be avoided and stores and spare parts secured and stowed.*
Cleaning	*Cleaning routines and equipment (chemicals) should be appropriate to the location and type of surfaces being treated. Where surfaces are slippery after cleaning, barriers should be put in place and warning signs posted.*
Spillages	*Any spillages must be cleaned up immediately and effectively. Where areas are treated or slippery, barriers should be put in place and warning signs posted.*
Personal Safety	*Personnel must take responsibility for their own safety and should use common sense when using access ways, stairways and ladders. Hold the handrails, do not carry heavy loads or loads which require two hands, wear the correct footwear, safety harnesses where appropriate and use equipment belts.*
Environment	*Even in port, ships can be an ever changing environment as cargo or fuel is loaded or discharged. Personnel must always consider the potential for unexpected movements onboard.*
Working Practices	*Equipment should be positioned to avoid trip hazards, use cable ramps, post signs, barrier off and restrict access to working areas.*
Shipboard Operations	*Personnel not involved with specific shipboard operations, such as mooring or cargo handling, should keep clear of the working area.*

6 Watertight Doors

Watertight doors are found on most seagoing vessels and powered watertight doors are commonplace, particularly on cruise liners, RoRo ferries and pipe and cable layers where machinery and working areas may extend almost the full length of the vessel. The installation of watertight bulkheads (fitted with watertight doors) sub-divides the vessel into a series of compartments to comply with watertight integrity and damage stability requirements.

There are two possible hazards:

- Failure to operate the watertight doors correctly or failure to follow opening procedures can lead to serious or fatal injuries to individuals

- failure to maintain the watertight doors in the closed position can result in a substantial loss of watertight integrity that can lead to considerable loss of life in the most extreme of cases.

All personnel should be made aware of the purpose of watertight doors.

6.1 Regulations and Watertight Integrity

International Maritime Organization

International Convention for the Safety of Life at Sea (SOLAS) Chapter II-1

http://shippingregs.org/18.re

SOLAS Chapter II-1, Regulation 25-9 (Openings in watertight bulkheads and internal decks in cargo ships) states:

"doors provided to ensure the watertight integrity of internal openings which are used while at sea are to be sliding watertight doors capable of being remotely closed from the bridge and are also to be operable locally from each side of the bulkhead. Indicators are to be provided at the control positions showing whether the doors are open or closed, and an audible alarm is to be provided at the door closure. Each power-operated sliding watertight door shall be provided with an individual hand-operated mechanism. It shall be possible to open and close the door itself from both sides."

Figure 6.1
Power-operated watertight door

SOLAS Chapter II-1, Regulation 15 (Openings in watertight bulkheads in passenger ships) states:

> *"the number of openings in watertight bulkheads shall be reduced to the minimum compatible with the design and proper working of the ship"* and *"shall be power-operated sliding doors capable of being closed simultaneously from the central operating console at the navigation bridge in not more than 60 seconds with the ship in the upright position"*.

> Further, it shall be possible to *"open and close the door by hand at the door itself from either side"* and *"shall be provided with an audible alarm, distinct from any other alarm in the area, which will sound whenever the door is closed remotely by power and which shall sound for at least 5 seconds but not more than 10 seconds before the door begins to move and shall continue sounding until the door is completely closed"*.

The SOLAS requirements do allow for watertight doors to be opened, while at sea, to permit safe access for passengers or crew or to allow work to be performed that may be impeded by the closure of the watertight door. However, any watertight door opened for such activities should be closed as soon as possible after completion of the access or work.

In special circumstances, watertight doors may be allowed to remain open for all parts of a transit at sea. These circumstances should be assessed and will only be allowable by consultation with the Flag State Authority.

Figure 6.2
Watertight integrity is of paramount importance on all vessels, but particularly ferries with bow and/or stern doors

6.2 Categorisation of Watertight Doors (MCA)

In complying with SOLAS requirements, the Maritime and Coastguard Agency (MCA) categorises watertight doors into three types. In addition, the MCA specifies two different scenarios for watertight doors; potentially hazardous situations and normal conditions.

Potentially hazardous situations include:

- Conditions of restricted visibility

- on any part of a voyage within port limits or within compulsory pilotage limits

- where the depth of water is less than three times the ship's draught

- in a situation that the Master considers potentially hazardous due to the proximity of underwater hazards or due to the density of the traffic in the area.

This risk-based approach adopted by the MCA, which allows some watertight doors to be kept open during normal sea conditions, has been introduced in an attempt to balance the need to maintain a vessel's watertight integrity with routine access requirements of the crew.

MCA Categorisation in Normal Conditions	
Type	MCA Instructions
A	May be kept open
B	Must be closed but may be open but only whilst someone is working in the compartment adjacent
C	Must be closed but may be opened but only for sufficient time to permit someone to pass through

MCA Categorisation in Potentially Hazardous Situations	
Type	MCA Instructions
A	Must be kept closed, except where a person is passing through it
B	Must be kept closed, except where a person is passing through it
C	Must be kept closed, except where a person is passing through it

6.3   Modes of Operation

Watertight doors can be operated locally or remotely.

Local control, where doors are operated by the controls at the watertight door, is the usual type. This active intervention to open and close reduces the risk of injury due to entrapment.

Remote control should only be used in emergency situations or when drills and training are being performed. In the remote control mode, the watertight doors can still be opened manually at the local control, but as soon as the operating controls are released, the watertight door will automatically return to the closed position. Routinely leaving the doors under remote control is, therefore, not a safe practice.

The control mode selected for the doors should not dictate the position of the doors. When at sea, under normal or potentially hazardous conditions, the doors should be closed and in local control. The fact that any persons passing through the watertight door will have to manually close it is irrelevant.

Figure 6.3
The dangers must be highlighted

6.4 Good Working Practices

Maritime and
Coastguard Agency

Marine Guidance Note
35 (M+F) Accidents
when using Power
Operated Watertight
Doors

http://shippingregs.org/21.re

Good working practices onboard are
essential to ensure the safe operation
of watertight doors:

- All new personnel assigned to a
  vessel should be made familiar
  with the position of all applicable
  watertight doors, their modes
  of operation and the correct
  procedure for transiting them

- all personnel should be made
  aware of the potential hazards
  associated with the use of
  watertight doors, particularly
  when under remote control.
  The importance of maintaining
  watertight integrity should be
  emphasised

- only trained personnel should
  operate them and refresher training
  should be performed at regular
  intervals

- warning notices highlighting
  the potential hazards should be
  prominently posted adjacent to all
  watertight doors

- remote control should only be used
  when conducting training, drills or
  in an emergency situation

- a clear and concise procedure
  should be in place, which should
  be made available on both sides of
  each and every watertight door

- the operating procedure should
  dictate that no person should transit
  a watertight door when carrying a
  load. Both hands should be free
  at all times to operate the control
  levers. Such operations should be
  a two-man task

- the operating procedure for
  the watertight doors should,
  irrespective of mode of operation,
  require the operator to fully open
  the door utilising the nearside
  control. Once the door is fully
  open, with one hand still holding
  the nearside control in the open
  position, the operator should reach
  through the opening with the other

hand and hold the far-side handle in the open position. The operator can then step through the doorway. Once completely on the other side, the controls can be released

■ watertight doors onboard must be kept in the recommended positions while at sea

■ housekeeping around watertight doors is essential and decks should be clean and free of any slip or trip hazards to prevent any persons slipping or tripping while transiting a watertight door

■ regular fire drills should include checks to verify the operation of watertight doors. Drills can also be used to re-familiarise crew with their use.

6.5 Incidents and Accidents

Accidents involving watertight doors have resulted in serious injury and fatalities.

Investigations into the accidents have identified a number of contributory factors:

■ Personnel unfamiliar with the modes of operation

■ personnel unfamiliar with SOLAS requirements for watertight integrity

■ overly complicated designs of watertight doors, where the operation is not fully understood by personnel

■ inadequate signs and instructions at the local control location

■ a lack of visual indications at the local control location to indicate the current mode of operation (remote or local).

SOLAS requirements for passenger ships address some of these contributory factors, but they do not apply to all vessel types.

Case Study: *'Eurovoyager'*

The *'Eurovoyager'* was purpose-built in 1978 as the *'Prins Albert'*. She commenced working on the Ramsgate to Ostend ferry route in 1994 and by 1998 was owned by Denval Marine Consultants and operated initially for Sally Line and then Transeuropa Ferries.

Incident Summary

At the time of the accident, the *'Eurovoyager'* was on a regular transit between Ostend, Belgium and Ramsgate in the United Kingdom. The regular routine was for the vessel to complete two return voyages between the ports each day.

MAIB Report No. 17/2009

 Report on the investigation of the entrapment of an engine room fitter in a watertight door onboard the RoRo passenger ship *'Eurovoyager'*

---

http://shippingregs.org/22.re

Prior to the accident, the vessel departed Ostend at approximately 07:50 hrs on 3rd November 2008.

Shortly after departure, the Master made a public address system announcement to advise all onboard that the watertight doors were to be closed. As part of this operation, the Master switched the watertight doors to the remote control panel on the bridge.

Later in the morning, the engine room fitter left the engine room for the changing room, operating three watertight doors as he did so. Once changed, he had to negotiate another watertight door to gain access to the auxiliary engine room and then the accommodation. At approximately 11:26 hrs, the fitter became trapped between the frame and the door assembly of the watertight door.

The fitter was found by the duty motorman within a few minutes and immediately released. He was unconscious.

Once the alarm had been raised, the Master switched the watertight doors from remote (bridge) to local control. Although attempts were made to evacuate the injured man by helicopter direct from the vessel, as the 'Eurovoyager' was so close to Ramsgate, the vessel berthed and he was then immediately taken by a waiting helicopter to hospital. It would be six months before he was able to return to work.

Incident Investigation

The investigation into the accident onboard the 'Eurovoyager' highlighted a number of factors that contributed to the potentially fatal incident:

- SOLAS requires that, at sea, watertight doors should be switched to local control. At the time of the incident, the watertight doors on the vessel were switched to remote control, so the door closed automatically on release of the local control handle

- it was a requirement of the SMS, and standard practice, for the watertight doors on the vessel to be switched to local control. However, due to an ongoing inspection on the vessel, this standard practice was not followed

- there was no visual (or other) indication at the watertight door to show whether the watertight door was in remote or local control. At the time of the incident, and also at the time of writing, this was not a SOLAS requirement

- the rate of closure of the watertight door, although acceptable for that vessel, was almost three times faster than that acceptable on new build vessels

- procedures for operating watertight doors onboard the vessel were in place. However, these were not sufficiently monitored or enforced

- from the position he was found in, it was surmised that the fitter could not have followed the watertight door operating procedures and that the door had not been fully open when he attempted to transit it

- no instructions or guidance was provided in the SOLAS training manual with regard to the safe operation of watertight doors

- the instructions (signage) on the bridge remote operating console were incorrect

- emergency operating procedures and instructions were displayed on both sides of the watertight door. However, these instructions did not state that the door had to be opened fully before passing through it, nor was there any indication of the potential dangers of entrapment.

Other significant factors that were highlighted, that did not contribute to the accident but which are of concern, included:

- The fitter was an experienced seafarer with more then twenty years experience, the majority of which had been served onboard RoRo passenger vessels. The incident highlights the fact that watertight doors pose a considerable hazard to even the most experienced of seafarers

- the fitter had been provided with a safety induction and familiarisation programme, which included a demonstration of the safe operation of watertight doors. Although this induction had been completed, the fitter still failed to follow the procedure

- the VDR indicated that the watertight doors were routinely left in the open position during transits. This practice could

have compromised the vessel's watertight integrity. The potential consequences from such practices are made clear by the 'Express Samina' disaster.

It is clear from the incident findings that watertight doors pose a potential risk for personnel required to transit them on a regular basis. However, the incident also highlights the fact that if the watertight doors were operated in the correct operational mode (local), and had the injured party operated the door using the correct procedure, this incident could have been easily avoided.

Case Study: 'Express Samina'

The incident involving the 'Express Samina' highlights a different hazard.

The 'Express Samina' was a passenger RoRo ferry, purpose-built in 1966. Originally named 'Corse', the vessel was owned and operated by a number of different French and Greek shipping companies until she was finally named 'Express Samina' in 1999. At this time she was operating in the Aegean.

Incident Summary

The 'Express Samina' departed Piraeus at approximately 17:00 hrs, bound for the Island of Paros.

The incident occurred late in the evening of 26th September 2000 as the vessel approached the Paros Harbour. The RoRo struck a well-lit, well-known and charted outcrop of rock, causing damage both below and above the waterline.

With the hull damaged, water ingress into the engine room was immediate and, due to the fact that a number of watertight doors were left open, spread progressively through the below deck compartments.

The vessel sank rapidly and, although it was very close to land, gale force winds hindered the rescue operation. 82 passengers and crew lost their lives, despite the best efforts of the many fishing vessels and larger ships, that attended the scene.

Incident Investigation

The investigation into the sinking of the 'Express Samina' was straightforward. Although there was large loss of life,

the majority of the crew, including the Master and hundreds of passengers, survived the tragedy so there were many witnesses able to testify and provide valuable information to assist the investigation team.

The initial navigational error, which caused the vessel to ground on the outcrop, was the cause of the incident. However, had the vessel's watertight doors all been closed at the time of the grounding, it would have remained afloat and the loss of life would have been minimal. Nine of the eleven watertight doors were open, allowing the rapid ingress of water. Calculations performed by the investigators confirmed that this was the case and that the damage stability condition of the vessel would not have been sufficient for the vessel to sink unless the watertight doors were open.

Progressive flooding through the open watertight doors was, therefore, found to be the main reason for loss of the 'Express Samina'.

7 Housekeeping and Hygiene

It is essential that good housekeeping and hygiene standards are maintained to ensure a safe working environment for crew members and a safe living environment for both crew and passengers. Poor housekeeping and hygiene standards can pose a serious risk of accident or hazard to health.

7.1 General Housekeeping

Good housekeeping standards should not be limited to specific areas.

Poor housekeeping includes:

- Temporary stowage of stores and spares

- inadequate removal of stores packaging

- inadequate securing of equipment

- inadequate stowage of paint and chemicals

- inadequate removal of oil or other spills

- inadequate removal of cargo dunnage

- inadequate removal of cargo residues

- inadequate control of tools.

Poor housekeeping levels can quickly result in the blocking of emergency exits, restriction of access to essential safety equipment or, in extreme cases, cause damage to equipment through shifting in heavy weather.

Temporary stowing of equipment, stores and spares can restrict general safe movement onboard ship and pose significant trip hazards, particularly when stowed in positions that are usually free of any obstruction.

Poor securing is a hazard that may not be significant while the vessel remains in port, but which may be considerably increased when in a moderate seaway.

Particular attention must be paid to good housekeeping practices where paints, chemicals or dangerous cargoes are concerned. Spillages from such substances can pose a considerable slip, fire or health hazard. Segregated stowage and adequate securing of paints, chemicals and dangerous cargoes will be part of good housekeeping practice.

Figure 7.1
Unsecured chemicals can pose a threat to health and safety onboard

Maintenance activities provide one of the most challenging threats to good housekeeping if not conducted in a controlled manner. Equipment being dismantled, serviced and then returned to an operational status can result in loose items (tools and parts) adjacent to the worksite and traces of oil and grease residues on decks and walkways. Tools or parts left on crane booms or cargo hatches, for example, can pose a serious risk.

Good housekeeping will ensure:

- Safe access to life-saving appliances

- safe access to fire-fighting equipment

- clear and unobstructed emergency exits

- safe movement onboard

- avoidance of potential fire hazards

- avoidance of loose items moving on deck

- avoidance of potential dropped objects

- avoidance of potential slip and trip hazards

- access for operational purposes

- access for maintenance purposes.

7.2 Galley Housekeeping and Hygiene

The risk of bacterial contamination can be present in well maintained galleys if working practices are poor.

Figure 7.2
Galley hygiene is essential

Causes include poor personal hygiene, infestation or as a result of poor storage and preparation.

The 1946 ILO Food and Catering (Ships' Crew) Convention does not contain any specific guidance, but sets out specific standards that should be maintained to provide a proper standard of food supply and catering service for crews on seagoing ships.

These minimum standards require that each nation state should develop, implement and enforce regulations concerning food and water supplies, catering, and the construction, location, ventilation, heating, lighting, water system and equipment in galleys and other associated spaces, including store rooms and refrigerated spaces.

Maritime and
Coastguard Agency

MGN 61 (M+F)
Guidelines for Food
Hygiene on Merchant
Ships and Fishing
Vessels

http://shippingregs.org/23.re

7.2.1 Personal Hygiene

Correct storage of foods will not prevent contamination if poor levels of personal hygiene are present. All catering crew have a responsibility to maintain their own personal hygiene when working in the galley and during the storing, preparing and serving of food.

Sufficient separate hand wash basins and toilet facilities should be provided for the exclusive use of the catering crew. The hand wash facilities should be used on a frequent basis, particularly when entering the galley for the start of work, prior to handling any food, between handling raw and uncooked foodstuffs and after any toilet visits.

Protective clothing appropriate to the galley should be worn. Any personnel working with food should ensure that any open sores or cuts cannot come into direct contact with the food and are covered using colour coded waterproof plasters.

See also Section 7.5.

7.2.2 Food Storage

Bacteria will proliferate in warm, moist environments. Dry foodstuffs must, therefore, be stored in dry, clean and well ventilated spaces to prevent the growth of harmful bacteria.

Dry foodstuffs should be separated from any frozen or raw foodstuffs and should be stowed clear of the decks to avoid contamination. There should be a free flow of air to avoid areas of high moisture and help prevent infestation.

A basic rotation policy for dry foodstuffs will ensure that foods approaching their expiry date are used first. This will also help to avoid food wastage.

The large volumes of liquids transferred in and out of the food stores pose a potential slip hazard and all areas should, therefore, be provided with suitable anti-slip flooring.

Figure 7.3
Food should not be stowed on the deck

7.2.3 Food Storage (Temperature Controlled)

Temperature controlled store rooms should be maintained to a high level of cleanliness and with the same considerations as dry stores. All items should be stored above the deck plating and be protected from any possible contamination.

Possible contamination sources include other food stuffs. Raw food should be stored in separate spaces from, for example, dairy products. If this is not possible due to a lack of available room, all raw foods should be stored at the lowest level to avoid dripping and cross-contamination.

Temperature levels should be regularly checked with constant read-out thermometers provided. Refrigerated spaces should be maintained at a temperature below 5°C. Particular attention should be paid to the condition of the door seals.

Figure 7.4
Storage temperatures must be monitored closely

Personnel should only be exposed to such areas of extreme temperature for very short periods and should, if possible, work in groups to avoid the potential of being locked in. All refrigerated areas should be provided with an emergency alarm that is regularly tested.

7.2.4 Food Preparation

The foodstuffs that present the highest risks are meats and dairy products and these should not only be stored separately, but defrosted and prepared separately.

Thawing of raw meat and poultry should be conducted in designated and separate areas where the thawed liquid cannot cause cross-contamination. The thawing process should take place with the raw meat or poultry elevated so that the thawed liquid is safely removed into a drip tray and does not allow the meat or poultry to sit in the juices.

If possible, separate food preparation areas should be designated for different food stuffs, such as raw meat and vegetables, to avoid cross-contamination. This is not always possible with the small space often available in the galley however, so at a minimum, areas should be thoroughly cleaned between the preparations of different food stuffs. Separate colour coded chopping boards should be used and separate utensils for the different foodstuffs. These simple recommendations will ensure the avoidance of bacterial cross-contamination.

Chopping Board Colour Coding	
Red	Raw Meat
Blue	Raw Fish
Yellow	Cooked Meat
Green	Salad and Fruit
Brown	Vegetables
White	Bakery and Dairy

- Store chilled and frozen food quickly

- keep the galley clean

- wash hands thoroughly and regularly

- separate raw and cooked food

- keep the fridge temperature below 5°C

- keep the freezer temperature below -18°C

- defrost food in controlled conditions

- check 'use-by' dates

- cook food thoroughly

- keep hot food hot and cold food cold.

Figure 7.5
Cooking food until the core temperature is 75°C or above will ensure that harmful bacteria are destroyed

A cooking thermometer should always be used to ensure that food has been brought to a high enough temperature to kill bacteria.

All cooking instructions should be closely followed.

7.3 Galley Equipment

Galley equipment should be assessed following installation. The assessment should consider the use and maintenance of the equipment and the environment in which the equipment will be operated. Onboard ship, this should include consideration of the changing environment when in a seaway. For example, galley stoves should have range guard rails.

7.4 Housekeeping and Hygiene Inspections

Merchant Shipping (Crew Accommodation) Regulations

http://shippingregs.org/24.re

The Merchant Shipping (Crew Accommodation) Regulations require accommodation to be maintained in a clean and habitable condition. To verify and maintain this standard, the Master (or a delegated deputy) is required to inspect all areas (including the galley and store rooms) within the crew accommodation at intervals not exceeding seven days. The Master should be accompanied by at least one member of the crew during this inspection and it is standard practice for the catering manager or Chief Steward to be in attendance.

Figure 7.6
Regular inspections will ensure higher standards

The completion of the inspection must be recorded in the official log book, along with any defects that indicate non-compliance with the Merchant Shipping (Crew Accommodation) Regulations.

7.5 Galley Safe Working Practices

Hazards associated with work in the galley and storage areas include:

- Slips, trips and falls
- cuts and burns
- electrocution.

Slip, Trips and Falls

Most injuries onboard any ship, and particularly to the catering staff, are likely to be caused as a result of a slip, trip or fall.

Stores and equipment should be stowed securely and should not protrude into walkways and working areas at head and foot height.

Any spillages should be cleaned up as soon as possible.

If the floor is slippery, anti-slip mats may be used.

Catering crew should wear suitable footwear with anti-slip treads and protected toe caps, particularly when loading stores or transferring heavy items onboard.

Cuts and Burns

DANGER
Hot surface

Protection against cuts and burns can be provided by good working practices, equipment design and the use of appropriate personal protection equipment.

Cut injuries are a considerable hazard. Knives should be kept clean and sharp and be stored in a dedicated place. Magnetic holders should be avoided and consideration should be given to the movement of the vessel when considering storage options for knives and any other equipment. Suitable gloves (such as Kevlar) should be worn when cutting meat and fish. Knives should be held at an angle so that the blade slopes away from the fingers.

Burns from hot surfaces and foodstuffs are a considerable hazard in the galley. Good ergonomics are essential, ensuring that the galley stove is well positioned so that the cooks do not have to stretch across hot surfaces. Hot stoves should not be left unattended and care and attention should be given when handling hot pots and pans. Aprons may be used to provide protection against splash and burn injuries.

Electrocution

Electrocution in the galley can occur through failure to isolate electrical equipment during washing down, routine tasks or maintenance.

The assessment of galley equipment for compliance with the Safe Use of Work Equipment regulations will identify the required minimum levels of isolation and control required for all galley equipment. (See Chapter 12)

It should be possible to isolate the galley equipment when performing routine tasks and a permit to work system should be used where appropriate. (See Chapter 10)

7.6   Potable Water

The provision of clean potable or drinking water is critical and failure to manage it can lead to serious risks to the health of all onboard. A wide range of pathogens can be transmitted by contaminated potable water being loaded onboard, inadequate disinfection of potable water once on the ship, contamination from sewage or

poor design and construction of potable water tanks.

Failure to control the potable water supply and stored water onboard can lead to waterborne bacteria such as Legionella. Legionella bacteria not only affects humans following ingestion in drinking or potable water, it can also be transmitted to the respiratory system from water suspended in the air in the form of a fine mist, such as is created in showers. Legionnaires' disease is potentially fatal and numerous incidents have been reported on all types of ship.

Measures to control Legionnaires' disease include:

- Treating potable water to prescribed limits

- maintaining potable water within temperature limits

- ensuring that loading hoses are uncontaminated

- regular flushing of water systems.

Maritime and Coastguard Agency

MSN No.1214 Recommendations to Prevent Contamination of Ships' Freshwater Storage and Distribution Systems

http://shippingregs.org/25.re

7.6.1 *Potable Water Tanks and System*

Figure 7.7
Potable water tank entry points should be raised above deck level

The design and construction of potable water tanks and piping systems will be the responsibility of the shipyard and Classification Society during build.

Potable water systems, including the pumps should, where at all possible, be completely independent from any other pumping system, such as ballast lines. On smaller ships this may not be possible and such arrangements are acceptable provided that there is a non-return valve, back-flow preventer or air break between the potable water and any other system.

The tanks should be constructed and positioned to avoid contamination from other sources. Potable water tanks should, therefore, not be adjacent to fuel tanks or the outer hull of the

vessel, where contamination could occur in the case of corrosion or damage.

The internal construction of all potable water tanks should allow the tank to be completely emptied for cleaning, flushing and maintenance purposes.

Pipework from other sources, including sewage lines, should not be piped through the potable water tanks or in close proximity to the potable water tank manhole covers, ventilation pipes or other areas where contamination could be possible. Manhole access points should be clearly marked and should be positioned clear of decks to avoid contamination (see Figure 7.7).

Ventilation pipes from potable water tanks should be constructed to avoid potential contamination from external sources and should be of the gooseneck design. This design helps stop seawater entering the potable water tanks via the ventilation pipes on deck and should also include a corrosion resistant mesh screen.

The use of sounding pipes should be avoided as contamination may be possible. As an alternative, sight gauges should be provided to allow a visual indication of the water level. Where sounding pipes are fitted and manual soundings taken, the pipes should be positioned and protected to avoid contamination into the tanks. A dedicated sounding rod should be used to avoid cross-contamination from other tanks.

For sampling purposes, sample cocks should be provided.

7.6.2 Maintenance of Potable Water Tanks

Standard industry guidance recommends that potable water tanks are completely drained, ventilated, inspected and cleaned at intervals not exceeding twelve months.

Potable water tanks are enclosed spaces and should be inspected in accordance with all onboard entry into enclosed spaces procedures and the ship's permit to work system. (See Chapter 10)

All personnel inspecting and cleaning potable water tanks must use PPE appropriate to the task and such equipment (including footwear) should not have been used for any other task. This is to avoid cross-contamination. Similarly, personnel conducting potable water tank inspections and cleaning operations should not have any skin infections or communicable disorders.

The tanks should be inspected to evaluate the coating, the tank construction, condition of access points, ventilation, sounding pipes and tank suctions.

Any defects found during the inspection should be rectified and the tank re-coated as necessary. Any coating used in a potable water tank must be approved for that purpose. The cleaned tank and potable water system should be flushed through, filled and super chlorinated to a concentration of 50 ppm. The potable water should be left for a period of approximately 12 hours before the system is flushed through.

The tank can then be refilled with clean fresh water and chlorinated (0.2 ppm).

Potable water tanks should be thoroughly pumped dry and, where necessary, washed down with fresh water at six monthly intervals.

On a more regular basis (every three months), shower heads and all flexible pipe attachments should be thoroughly cleaned in a 50 ppm chlorine solution.

7.6.3 Loading of Potable Water

Sources of potable water:

- Loaded directly from a shore supply

- loaded from a shore supply via a barge

- produced onboard using a fresh water generator (evaporator).

Where potable water is loaded directly from a shore supply or from a barge, it is critical that only hoses dedicated to that supply are used. The hoses and associated connections should be colour coded to avoid cross-contamination.

Potable water hoses should be flushed through before use and on completion of loading operations. They should be thoroughly dried and stowed clear of the deck. When not in use, routine flushing and disinfection should be conducted at least every six months. The loading system onboard should be completely separate from any other systems (such as ballast) and should be blanked off when not in use.

If possible, the potable water hose should be connected and a test sample drained off prior to commencement of loading. If there are any concerns regarding the quality of the potable water it should not be loaded.

Potable water should not be loaded into the current service tank and should be isolated until it has been treated and accepted as satisfactory for use.

Potable water loaded from a shore supply or from a barge should be chlorinated to a residual chlorine content of 0.2 ppm. The dosage will depend on the tank capacity.

Maritime and Coastguard Agency

MSN No.1401 Disinfection of Ships' Domestic Fresh Water

http://shippingregs.org/26.re

Ship Captain's Medical Guide

http://shippingregs.org/27.re

Potable water can also be produced onboard using evaporators or a reverse osmosis plant.

As with a standard onboard potable water distribution system, the component parts of an evaporator system or reverse osmosis plant should all be inspected, cleaned and flushed on a regular basis. All components should be maintained in accordance with the manufacturer's instructions and should be incorporated into the planned maintenance system.

Legionella bacteria do not develop in seawater. Therefore, water produced by evaporation or a reverse osmosis plant does not have that particular risk.

Figure 7.8
Loading hoses and onboard pipe work should be colour coded

There are limitations to the use of reverse osmosis plants.

Reverse osmosis plants should not be used if there are any potential sources of contamination in close proximity to the vessel's seawater intakes. They should not be used in shallow water, enclosed sea areas, within the 500 m safety zone of offshore installations or in coastal areas, particularly in proximity to river and manmade outlets. If the vessel is stationary (at anchor or on DP), content pumped overboard may be drawn into the seawater intakes and, therefore, the reverse osmosis plant.

Case Study: *'Black Watch'*

The *'Black Watch'* is a passenger vessel built in 1972 as the *'Royal Viking Star'*. The vessel has been upgraded a number of times and has a total passenger capacity of 868. In addition the vessel can carry over 300 crew.

Incident Summary

An outbreak of respiratory infection among passengers on the *'Black Watch'* occurred between 15th July and 1st August 2007. At the time, the vessel had 756 passengers and 329 crew. The majority of the passengers were elderly and, of these, 12 had to be transferred from the ship to shore hospitals with respiratory problems. A least a further 40 passengers were also treated onboard the ship. Among the affected passengers, it has been reported that there were cases of Legionnaires' disease, which were traced to onboard showers and spa pools.

8 Personal Protective Equipment (PPE)

8.1 Introduction

All personnel must accept responsibility for selecting and wearing the appropriate PPE for the task.

Personal protective equipment (PPE) is defined by the United Kingdom Health and Safety Executive Personal Protective Equipment at Work Regulations 1992 (amended) as:

"all equipment (including clothing affording protection against the weather) which is intended to be worn or held by a person at work and which protects him against one or more risks to his health or safety"

Although PPE is considered as a final control measure it is an essential element in ensuring safety onboard any ship for both routine and non-routine activities. The correct use and maintenance of such equipment is necessary to ensuring its effectiveness and in the fostering and maintenance of a positive safety culture.

Personal Protective Equipment

"Personal protective equipment must be used only when risks cannot be avoided or reduced to an acceptable level by safe working practices, that cause no health risk to any worker."

COSWP, 2010, *www.dft.gov.uk/mca*

8.2 Regulations and Guidance

International organisations that regulate maritime health matters and PPE include the following:

- World Health Organization (WHO)
  The International Health Regulations 2005 define the obligations, rights and procedures of WHO member states for the prevention and spread of disease.

- International Maritime Organization (IMO)
  Standards of Training and Certification of Watchkeeping Convention 1995 (STCW) specifies the training and competence standards required for seafarers in relation to the use of personal protective equipment, including LSA, fire-fighting, first aid and PPE.

- International Labour Organization (ILO)
  The impending Maritime Labour Convention 2006 (MLC) has at the time of writing not yet been ratified. The convention encompasses and updates 68 existing ILO conventions which include standards required of the competent authority relating to seafarers' health and safety protection including PPE.

In the UK a memorandum of understanding exists between the three main organisations to ensure coordination where their duties concerning health and safety overlap. The three organisations and their powers and responsibilities are outlined as follows.

MCA surveyors *appointed under section 256 of the 1995 Act have powers under Section 258 of that Act to inspect UK ships (anywhere in the world) as well as foreign vessels whilst in UK waters (this does not apply to non-UK ships on innocent passage). MCA's interest is in the seaworthiness of the vessel, the safety and competence of the crew and as a prosecuting authority. Surveyors may detain unsafe ships. Section 256 of the 1995 Act provides for the appointment of inspectors who, under section 259 of the Act, have additional powers including the power to enter any premises in the UK, for the purposes of making such examination or inspection as the inspector considers necessary. Inspectors may issue improvement or prohibition notices in respect of any regulated activity. (However not all surveyors are appointed as inspectors). Departmental Inspectors investigate incidents with a view to prosecution.*

MAIB inspectors *have powers to investigate accidents involving or occurring on board UK ships (anywhere in the world), and any ships in the UK territorial sea. They are appointed under section 267 of the Merchant Shipping Act 1995 and have the power under section 259 to enter any premises in the UK or board any UK ship wherever it may be in the world and any other ship which is present in the UK or in UK waters for the purposes of making such examination or inspection as the inspector considers necessary. MAIB inspectors do not have the power to prosecute or otherwise bring disciplinary proceedings for unsafe working practices.*

HSE inspectors *derive their powers principally from Sections 20-23 of HSWA and associated legislation. They have, for example, power of entry to all work places, including docks and offshore installations, to inspect health and safety conditions and also to investigate accidents to dock workers etc working in a port or while loading or unloading a ship. They can similarly investigate accidents occurring to a ship's crew. They may issue improvement or prohibition notices, or can prosecute those responsible for offences under HSWA and the relevant statutory provisions.*

www.maib.gov.uk

For United Kingdom registered vessels and for vessels operating within United Kingdom waters, there are two important pieces of legislation; the Health and Safety Executive Personal Protective Equipment at Work Regulations and the Merchant Shipping and Fishing Vessels (Personal Protective Equipment) Regulations 1999. Both sources are similar in purpose and scope and reflect the requirements of wider European regulations as detailed in European Directive 89/686/EEC.

Regulatory explanation and guidance is provided by the MCA, through The Stationary Office, in the publication The Code of Safe Working Practices for

Merchant Seamen (COSWP). Up-to-date copies of this book must be carried onboard all UK merchant ships, and any seafarer requesting the book should have a copy made available to them.

Requirements, standards and responsibilities for employers and workers onboard United Kingdom ships are explained in MSN 1731. In addition to describing the standards for PPE regarding EN and BS specifications, the following is stated:

1. The Regulations require employers to ensure that personal protective equipment (PPE) is provided for their workers who are engaged in, or at risk from, a hazardous work activity onboard a United Kingdom ship.

2. The Regulations are subject to the general rule that use of PPE is always a last resort, where risks cannot be avoided or reduced to a safe level by means of collective protection, or safe systems of work.

3. PPE must be provided free of charge to the workers, except that, where use of the equipment is not exclusive to the work place, workers may be required to contribute towards the cost.

4. Where, traditionally, workers provide their own PPE, the employer remains responsible for ensuring that workers are equipped with appropriate PPE, and that they use it when engaged in work of the types outlined in Annex 1.

5. The equipment issued must be "suitable", which is defined as:

(a) in relation to any work process described in [this] Merchant Shipping Notice MSN 1731(M+F), of the kind and to the standard specified [in that Merchant Shipping Notice], in relation to that work process;

(b) appropriate for the risks to which the worker is exposed and to the task which he is performing, without itself leading to any increased risk;

(c) correctly fitting the worker, or capable of being adjusted to fit;

(d) taking into account ergonomic requirements and the worker's state of health;and

(e) compatible with any other equipment the worker has to use at the same time, so that it continues to be effective against the risk.

6. In addition, the employer must ensure that the PPE supplied is easily accessible, and properly stored and maintained, and that where appropriate, instructions are available to the workers who are required to carry out any maintenance. The equipment must be regularly inspected, in accordance with the manufacturer's instructions, and its operation checked. Respiratory protective equipment must always be checked before and after use.

7. The employer must ensure, so far as is reasonably practicable, that PPE issued under the regulations is used as instructed - eg that workers do not use it for a purpose for which it is not designed, and that it is put on and worn correctly.

8. Workers must receive adequate and appropriate training so that they are aware of the risks against which the PPE is designed to protect them, and of when and how to use it and look after it correctly. This may include demonstrations of the wearing of PPE, where appropriate.

9. Workers are required to wear and use the PPE which has been issued to them when appropriate, and to comply with any training and instruction provided.

8.3 Purpose of PPE

PPE provides protection against the potential hazard(s) associated with the task being performed. The type(s) of PPE to be used will depend on the task being conducted, the particular circumstances and environmental conditions at the time. Such equipment may include:

- Safety helmets

- eye protection

- ear protection

- respiratory equipment

- protective clothing

- protective gloves

- safety footwear

- buoyancy aids

- safety harnesses.

When more than one item of PPE is used all equipment must be compatible and suited to the intended task. Where the PPE impacts on the task, eg impaired mobility when using respiratory equipment, then it must be fully considered and assessed during the risk assessment. PPE is not a substitute for other precautions or control measures and is only used as a final resort.

Figure 8.1
PPE is essential for many shipboard tasks

 Maritime and Coastguard Agency

The Merchant Shipping and Fishing Vessels (Personal Protective Equipment) Regulations

http://shippingregs.org/28.re

8.4 Types of PPE

There are two basic types of PPE; *simple* and *complex*. Simple PPE is equipment that can be immediately understood and worn by the user without the need for any instruction or training and protects the user against minor risks to health and safety. Complex PPE is used to describe equipment that protects the user against more substantial risks to health and safety and which requires instruction and guidance to be provided to the user, eg respiratory devices. In addition, equipment that may have interchangeable components, such as face masks, would also be considered as complex.

Hazard	Type of PPE
Dropped objects, moving objects or obstructions	*Head protection*
Welding, cutting, dust particles, chemicals, paint	*Eye and face protection*
Dust particles, vapours, gases, oxygen deficient atmosphere, paint	*Respiratory protection*
Noise from machinery and operations	*Ear protection*
Welding, cutting, chemicals, heat, cold, environmental aspects, paint, operations (visibility)	*Body protection*
Chemicals, heat, cold, electrical equipment, abrasion, paint, cuts, skin infection and disease	*Hand and finger protection*

Dropped objects or moving objects, welding, cutting, chemicals, slippery surfaces and spills	*Foot protection*
Working aloft, in exposed positions (including in enclosed spaces)	*Fall protection*
Working overside or in exposed positions	*Buoyancy aids*

It is advisable that minimum PPE requirements are set for certain areas of the vessel to ensure all personnel (including visitors) are protected.

8.5 Selection of PPE

Appropriate PPE will depend on the task to be performed, the environment in which the task is to be conducted and on the hazards identified during the risk assessment. Identification of hazards will dictate the type and grade of equipment required to ensure they fulfil their primary function. For example, boots may be required to prevent slippage or injury from falling equipment, but they may also need to provide resistance to any potential substances or solvents that will damage the material and degrade their effectiveness. Where equipment is complex or new to the user, appropriate training should be provided to ensure it is used/worn correctly, used appropriately and limitations understood.

Annex 1 of MSN 1731 provides the standards of PPE that are appropriate to specified work activities for UK vessels and provide practical guidance for all vessels (Appendix 1).

However, all PPE should conform to some basic fundamental standards and should:

- Be appropriate for the risks to which the worker will be exposed for the proposed task

- be suitable for the environmental conditions at the intended worksite and should take into consideration the expected duration of use, wear and the effects on the PPE during the task

- be suitable in relation to any substances, such as chemicals, that may be handled as part of the intended task. The type of PPE should consider any hazards associated with such chemicals and not increase any identified risks or create any further risks to the safety of the personnel

- be compatible with other equipment used and the ergonomics of the work place. Where more than one item of PPE is utilised, the effectiveness of all items must be maintained

- be provided with working instructions for use and maintenance

- be maintained in accordance with the manufacturer's instructions and with due regard to the environmental conditions and level of use onboard

- be stored in a protected and dedicated storage area to ensure that the equipment is not exposed to chemicals or other sources of contamination, including seawater and direct sunlight

- be inspected prior to and on completion of use. Any damaged or defective PPE should be replaced as appropriate

- be designed and manufactured with due regard to ergonomic considerations and the health requirements of the worker. No PPE should pose a risk to the health or safety of the wearer and should allow the wearer to adapt the equipment to suit their own build. PPE should not restrict the mobility or visibility of the wearer.

Head Protection

Head protection should be worn during any process or activity where there is a reasonably foreseeable risk to the head.

Head injuries can be fatal and personnel can be at risk from this type of injury from a variety of shipboard operations:

- Any activity that involves working below other personnel or fixed or temporary equipment, introduces the risk of injury from falling objects or substances

- any task in the vicinity of moving machinery, eg during lifeboat training, that introduces a risk from contact with moving parts

- working at height or within enclosed spaces with the potential for trips, slips or falls adds a risk of injury

- operational tasks such as cargo, anchoring or mooring operations pose a potential risk of head injuries.

There are a number of places onboard any vessel where potential head injury risks may be evident, including the engine room spaces, cargo decks, holds and within tanks. Any enclosed space or restricted area will provide potential areas where low beams or pipes, as examples, may be introduced.

Safety helmets are ordinarily required to be of a seamless single shell construction. A harness that can be adjusted to the user should connect securely to the shell, providing a gap between the shell and head to absorb impact.

While safety helmets provide protection against impact injury they can also provide degrees of protection against crushing or chemical splashes. Similarly bump caps, although offering a lesser degree of protection, can be considered suitable for jobs with a lesser degree of risk. Safety caps or hair nets are another form of head

protection for crew with long hair working with machinery that has a risk of entanglement.

Head protection can therefore be applicable to many onboard operations and tasks and suitable protection should be provided and utilised. The selection of appropriate equipment, such as safety helmets with integrated ear protection for the engine room or safety helmets with high visibility covers for the main deck, will be dependent on the location of the task and the potential risks.

Personal Responsibility

All personnel must accept responsibility for selecting and wearing the appropriate PPE for the task

---

Figure 8.2
PPE standards are an important part of a good safety culture and working environment

Eye and Face Protection

Eye and face protection should be worn during any process or activity where there is a reasonably foreseeable risk to the eyes or the face

While there may be specific risks associated with certain cargoes, eg bulk carriers, gas carriers or chemical tankers, eye injuries can occur from a number of tasks onboard any vessel. Eye injuries can be irreversible and facial injuries traumatic. Eye and facial injuries can result from:

- Work activities such as painting, shot blasting, welding or cutting operations

- the use of fixed and portable hand tools such as drills and grinders

- work involving the use of chemicals

- dust particles or vapours.

It should also be considered that there may be risks to personnel not involved directly with the particular work activity if such operations are being conducted in close proximity to walkways and access ways.

The selection of the appropriate eye and face protection will depend on the task and the associated residual risks, following implementation of all other control measures. Equipment includes:

- Safety spectacles – toughened glasses with or without side shields

- safety goggles – constructed of flexible plastic with an elasticated headstrap

- eye shields – normally a moulded box type of lens worn over ordinary spectacles

- face shields – designed to protect the full face. As they are not normally sealed, they are unlikely to protect against dust, vapour or gas.

Operations such as welding require degrees of shading due to the bright intensity of the work and potential damage to the eye. The effects are commonly known as arc eye (caused by the UV rays from electric arc welding) or welder's flash caused by infrared rays from gas welding. Similarly, sunglasses provide protection against photokeratitis, also known as ultraviolet (UV) keratitis or snowblindess, which can be caused by sunlight reflected from surfaces such as the sea or ice.

The eye and face protection selected should protect all vulnerable parts of the face and should be of a design and construction that will prevent injury from the equipment and substances being used. For example, some safety goggles may not be designed for contact with chemicals. Only protective equipment designed and manufactured for the intended task should be used. Face shields or full face visors should be used where full protection is required.

In all circumstances, all eye and face protection must be adjustable and suitable for the user.

Figure 8.3
Eye protection should be appropriate for the task

Figure 8.4
Eye damage may be irreversible

Respiratory Protection

Respiratory protection should be worn by all personnel when conducting work in an atmosphere that may be hazardous to their health

There are many activities onboard ship where the atmosphere may be hazardous to personnel. Such activities can include painting, grit blasting, burning, cutting and welding operations and any other task where dust particles may be in the atmosphere. For these types of task, personnel may utilise dust masks or respirators as appropriate.

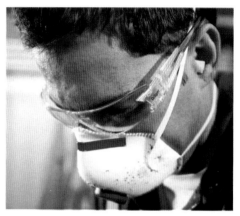

Figure 8.5
Disposable dust mask

Respirators filter the air and can protect the user from the immediate effects of inhalation of dusts, particles and the diseases that can be caused by long-term exposure. Respirators do not protect the user from oxygen deficient atmospheres and should not be used as protection for enclosed spaces. Respirators are constructed using

Figure 8.6 (a)
Dust respirator

cartridges, canisters and filters from specific materials to protect against identified hazards. Cartridges, canisters and filters must be replaced regularly, as per the manufacturer's instructions. When selecting the type of respirator the hazards identified in the risk assessment will dictate the type required:

- Dust respirator – generally of half mask construction that covers the nose and mouth, often of a simple lightweight construction. They protect against dust or aerosol sprays (eg paint)

- positive pressure respirator – has a battery powered unit that blows air (via a tube) to create positive pressure and prevent external air ingress

- cartridge respirator – either half or a full face mask, with a replaceable cartridge and filter. Used mainly for low toxicity vapours

- canister respirator – a full face mask connected to a separate canister providing greater protection against toxic vapours.

Figure 8.6 (b)
Positive pressure respirator

Figure 8.6 (c)
Canister respirator

Respiratory protection includes the use of breathing devices, such as breathing apparatus which provide a clean supply of air. This equipment is used where there may be an oxygen deficient atmosphere or the presence of toxic fumes is suspected.

Figure 8.7
Breathing apparatus is used where there may be an oxygen deficient atmosphere

It is particularly important that the seal and fitting of respirators and breathing apparatus prevents any leakage. Special attention should be paid to any person with a beard as it is unlikely that a proper seal will be achieved. Similarly, spectacles can also create problems when wearing respiratory equipment.

Ear Protection

 The IMO Code on Noise Levels on Board Ships states that hearing protection should be worn when entering or working in a space or working with machinery or equipment where the noise level exceeds 85 Db(A)

In addition to the PPE Regulations, it should be noted that there are specific regulatory requirements in the form of the Noise at Work Regulations and the IMO Resolution A.864 (XII) Code on Noise Levels on Board Ships relating to ear protection.

Maximum Noise Levels (IMO)	
Work Space	**dB(A)**
Machinery spaces (continuously manned)	90
Machinery spaces (not continuously manned)	110
Machinery control rooms	75
Workshops	85
Non-specified work spaces	90

IMO resolution A.486(XII) Code on Noise Levels on Board Ships (1981)

Where the noise level is above 85 dB(A) ear protection should be provided and the limit of 110 dB assumes that ear protection is worn when in the space.

With the exception of 'normally unoccupied spaces' where a limit of 90 dB(A) is imposed, other areas, ie service, accommodation and navigation spaces, have limits set that do not exceed 85 dB(A) and so do not require ear protectors.

As with other forms of PPE it is the duty of the employer to reduce the risk to the health and safety of the seafarer by all appropriate means available. Ear protection should be considered as the last available measure to protect the individual.

Noise levels should be primarily controlled by design and engineering, adapting the working environment and by providing equipment that produces the least noise possible. However, even if all these factors are taken into consideration, there may be circumstances where seafarers are exposed to high noise levels for prolonged periods of time. Such exposure may be caused by fixed machinery (engine room) or where portable tools are being used. Under these conditions, there is the potential for permanent noise induced hearing loss.

Due regard must be given to the condition of ear protection to ensure that the equipment remains free from defects as damage can reduce its effectiveness. Risks to the health and hygiene of personnel exist through cross-contamination of ear plugs and to a lesser extent ear muffs. It is important that personnel are issued with their own dedicated ear protection or use disposable plugs.

International Maritime Organization

Code on Noise Levels on Board Ships

http://shippingregs.org/29.re

Figure 8.8
Ear protection must be worn in machinery spaces and all areas with high noise levels

Ear protection can be either disposable or permanent of the following types:

- Ear plugs – the simplest type that fit into the ear canal. In areas of high frequency they are prone to vibration which can reduce their effectiveness in the ear canal. It is recommended that they are of the disposable type and are not used by personnel with ear problems

- ear muffs – commonly constructed of rigid cups with padded surfaces and an adjustable headband, ear muffs offer greater protection.

Figure 8.9
Hearing damage can be permanent

Body Protection

Body protection should be worn to protect the user from direct contact with substances that may cause injury or harm.

Body protection is essential in all work areas and should provide complete protection commensurate with the task, environmental conditions and any substances being used. Body protection can include boiler suits (standard, lightweight and fire retardant), jackets, chemical suits, aprons and welding tunics.

Tasks such as welding, cutting and burning, painting and grit blasting are common to all ship types and require full body protection. Protection can also be in the form of high visibility clothing to ensure that the wearer is visible while performing certain operations. This could include loading operations on a RoRo, platform supply vessel or container ship, where ensuring the visibility of personnel to drivers and crane operators is essential. In such circumstances a high visibility vest or jacket may also be necessary rather than simply reflective banding on a boiler suit.

Figure 8.10
High visibility vests or jackets ensure the wearer can be seen during potentially hazardous operations

Environmental conditions can include extremes of temperature from arctic to tropical conditions. Failure to provide suitable body protection in extreme temperatures can have serious consequences. Similarly, the provision of unsuitable heavy weather clothing to protect personnel during adverse weather conditions can pose serious health hazards to the individual.

Where potential exists for a person to fall overboard through the vessel's operations, eg AHTS or EERVs then flotation/immersion suits must be considered. These should be in addition to buoyancy vests if they are not integral to the suit. Such equipment must be maintained and serviced in accordance with the manufacturer's guidelines.

Environmental conditions can also be a consideration within the shipboard environment. Protective clothing for work on deck may not be suitable in the engine room and other machinery spaces where there is a greater risk of fire or exposure to heat and hot surfaces. Consideration should therefore be given to the use of flame retardant protective clothing in specific areas and the provision of protective clothing to galley staff who are working in an area with hot surfaces and equipment.

Any task that requires the use of substances likely to cause harm through contact should be considered and body protection provided accordingly. This should include any specific cargoes or cargo residues and the use of chemical suits may be required.

Body protection should also offer protection against abrasion and direct contact with machinery parts. The clothing should be such that the potential for entanglement with machinery is avoided.

Hand and Finger Protection

 Hand and finger protection should be used in all circumstances where there is the potential for contact with harmful substances, chemical or thermal burns, abrasions, cuts, punctures or contact with equipment

Hands and fingers may be considered the most at risk part of the human body during routine operations onboard ship. Hands and fingers are most likely to come into contact with chemicals or cargo residues and are at the greatest risk from cuts, punctures or even loss through the use of machinery and other equipment.

The use of gloves is, in many circumstances, a necessity. In determining the type to be used, the potential hazards associated with the task should be considered and provide protection against:

- Chemicals and micro-organisms

- abrasion and penetration, ie cuts and puncture wounds

- high temperatures

- cold temperatures

- electrical shock

- mechanical risks.

Except where specialist substances are encountered, the following provide a general guide for types of gloves:

- Synthetic, PVC or rubber gloves are used when handling solvents or other substances. Latex allergies are common and sufficient alternatives should be considered when ordering supplies

- heat resistant gloves are required when contact with hot materials is likely

- leather gloves should be used where cuts and abrasions are likely.

For work in the galley when preparing food the main area of concern may be maintaining hygiene levels and ensuring no cross-contamination of foods. Gloves should be available for cleaning or other activities involving detergents which may have adverse dermatological effects. When using knives for food preparation, protection against cuts should be considered and good quality kitchen gloves should be provided for handling hot equipment.

Where the use of chemicals may be integral to the task, such as tank cleaning or cargo operations, consideration should be given to the properties of the substances and hazards from direct skin exposure. Gloves and other clothing manufactured from appropriate materials should be selected to ensure full protection.

Mooring operations involve direct contact with abrasive mooring ropes, so when gloves are used they should be properly fitted. Leather gloves provide protection when handling wires and sharp ends. However the risk of snagging and crushing injuries means looser fitting gloves may be considered to allow the glove to come free when snagged on a loose wire.

For electrical work and engineering tasks, hand and finger protection may need to be provided to protect against contact with live electrical equipment and against contact with extremes of temperature. An example of such is the use of rubber gloves when handling helicopter lines due to the high risk of static electricity.

When working in cold areas, gloves that provide warmth and prevent direct contact with very cold surfaces should be used.

Foot Protection

Foot protection should be worn when engaged in any activity in a work area where there may be the risk of injury to the feet or where there may be slip, trip or fall hazards

Suitable footwear is essential because in addition to avoiding discomfort from movement on hard steel decks it provides protection from:

- Slip, trips and falls

- dropped objects (crushing)

- penetration through the shoe's sole

- electrical hazards

- chemical hazards

- contact with abrasive and moving machinery.

Slip-resistant properties and impact-resistant toe caps are the most commonly accepted benefits of safety footwear, but electrical insulation, chemical resistance and protection to the ankles from falls is also provided by many boots.

In exterior and working areas, the use of anti-slip and reinforced footwear capable of providing protection against impacts and chemicals is required. However, even within accommodation areas, hazards from slips and trips remain considerable and are exacerbated by the movement of the ship. The use of inappropriate footwear such as open-toed sandals and flip-flops should therefore be discouraged. All personnel are strongly advised to wear appropriate safety footwear when working.

Health and Safety
Executive

Personal Protective
Equipment at Work
Regulations

http://shippingregs.org/30.re

Fall Protection

*Fall protection should be
worn in all circumstances
where there is a
foreseeable risk of injury
from a fall*

*Figure 8.11
Fall protection equipment must be worn
where any potential risk is foreseeable*

There are numerous activities onboard
all ships where personnel may be
required to wear fall protection
equipment. MSN 1731 and the COSWP
both indicate that suitable safety
equipment is required when there is a
risk of falling more than 2 metres. The
HSE does not specify a fall distance. It
is extremely important to be clear that
this does not only include situations
where personnel may be deemed to be
working at height. There are situations
where personnel may be at deck level

or even within tanks, but the risk of
a fall may be considerable. Some
examples of these circumstances are:

- Where hatches, access ways or
  deck openings are removed or
  are in the open position due to
  operational circumstances such as
  cargo loading or discharging

- overside work where there is the
  potential to fall clear of the ship,
  into the water or onto the quayside

- gangway, pilot or accommodation
  ladder rigging or unrigging
  operations where the safe means
  of access is being put in place or
  removed prior to departure

- work conducted in spaces such as
  cargo holds, ballast tanks or fuel
  tanks where there is a potential risk
  of injury due to a fall within the tank

- maintenance on cranes, derricks,
  masts or in the engine room.
  Maintenance work in the engine
  room should not be discounted
  from consideration as work at
  height will often be an integral part
  of maintenance routines.

Maritime and
Coastguard Agency
(MCA)

MGN 410 (M+F)
Work at Height
Regulations

http://shippingregs.org/31.re

The selection of fall protection
equipment type is vital and should be

determined by the risk assessment. The type of equipment includes:

- Work restraint – this comprises a lanyard that restricts the movement of users to safe areas, ie prevents the person getting too close to an edge

- work positioning – enables work to take place when suspended or under tension, eg a stage or bosun's chair. An additional safety line is required

- rope access – uses two ropes attached to a harness with one acting as a safety line. Ropework is used to access areas unsuitable for scaffolding or cradles

- fall arrest – used to prevent a person hitting the ground or to limit the force of impact.

As with all types of PPE, fall protection equipment used by individual personnel should be the last mitigation against risk. In all circumstances where there is potential for a fall from height, the task should be risk assessed, alternative methods of conducting the work should be considered and it should only be completed if essential. The use of collective control measures such as permanent or temporary guardrails should also be considered.

Work should only be carried out at height if there is no reasonably practicable alternative.

When fall arrest equipment is to be used for working at height:

- All personnel using fall arrestor equipment should be adequately trained and familiarised with the correct methods of use and any limitations of the equipment

- all working at height equipment should be regularly inspected, including prior to and on completion of the working at height task

- anchorage points should be suitable and certified for the task

- the risk assessment for the task should consider the methods to be used to rescue personnel in the event of an accident. Rescue plans are an integral part of working at height operations, as suspension trauma is a considerable hazard and a prompt rescue of persons must be possible

- in situations where personnel may be required to work over the side, buoyancy aids must also be worn.

The Merchant Shipping and Fishing Vessels (Work at Height) Regulations

http://shippingregs.org/32.re

Buoyancy Aids

Buoyancy aids should be worn whenever personnel are required to work overside or in positions where there is the potential to fall overside

Overside work will generally be for maintenance purposes such as painting. However, there will also be situations where work onboard is in an exposed position that creates a reasonably foreseeable risk of falling or being washed overboard. These circumstances may include gangway rigging operations or work in exposed areas of the deck, including lifeboat embarkation areas where there may be no collective measures such as guardrails.

Approved lifejackets and personal buoyancy aids will be required for a variety of circumstances and will often be worn at the same time as thermal protective clothing, fall arrestor equipment and other forms of PPE. Where this is the case, the equipment should be non-obstructive.

Whenever potential exists for a person to fall overboard, a lifebuoy with sufficient line should also be available for immediate use.

Case Study: *'Ville De Mars'*

The *'Ville de Mars'* is a container vessel that was built in Korea in 1990. She was operated by a French shipping company, registered in the UK and had a multi-national crew.

The incident onboard the *'Ville De Mars'* could, on first view, be more associated with the risks of entry into enclosed spaces. However, it also highlights an aspect of working at height that is often overlooked.

Marine Accident Investigation Branch (MAIB)

Report No 20/2009

http://shippingregs.org/33.re

Incident Summary

While on passage from Sri Lanka to the United Arab Emirates, the Chief Officer onboard the *'Ville de Mars'* died following a fall in a water ballast tank. The vessel was crossing the Gulf of Oman at the time and was due to arrive in port the following day. The incident took place on 28th January 2009.

The water ballast tank had a capacity of 406 m³ and was over 12 m in depth. There were two manholes allowing access to the tank, both located on the deck of one of the cargo holds. Access into both manhole covers was via vertical ladders. Guardrails were fitted in some places within the tank, but not all. Fall protection was, therefore, incomplete.

Prior to entering the water ballast tank, the Chief Officer had informed the Master of his intentions and had the Bosun and one able seaman with him to assist. The tank had been ventilated and the Chief Officer had an oxygen analyser. No permit to work was raised, nor was any consideration given to working at height procedures.

The Chief Officer advised the Third Officer, who was on the bridge, prior to entering the tank and tested the tank's atmosphere. The Bosun and able seaman remained at the tank entrance.

The Chief Officer entered the tank and descended the vertical ladder. He had a hand-held torch and a radio slung across his chest. The portable oxygen analyser and his camera were in his coverall pockets.

The Chief Officer was observed stopping at the 5th or 6th rung of the vertical ladder and taking another reading with the oxygen analyser, before stepping onto a stringer. Moments later the Bosun and able seaman heard a loud noise and looked into the tank to see the Chief Officer lying at the bottom of the tank.

The bridge was immediately informed and the Third Officer sounded the general alarm. The Master took control on the bridge and the third officer went to assist with the rescue operation.

The Bosun advised the rescue party that the Chief Officer had slipped and that the tank atmosphere was satisfactory. On the basis of this advice, up to 9 crew members entered the tank to attempt a rescue. They successfully recovered the unconscious, but still

breathing, Chief Officer to deck. Over the next few hours, the Chief Officer regained consciousness but had difficulty breathing and, at one point, the Second Officer had to perform cardio pulmonary resuscitation (CPR). By early afternoon, the Chief Officer had been examined by a doctor, winched onboard a Royal Navy helicopter and was immediately removed from the vessel for evacuation. He died en route to hospital in Oman.

Incident Investigation

There were no direct witnesses to the incident as neither the Bosun nor the able seaman witnessed the fatal fall. However, it was surmised that the Chief Officer had slipped off the unguarded edge of the stringer, possibly due to the deep layer of sludge present. It is not believed that the atmosphere within the tank was a contributory factor in the case.

During the subsequent incident investigation, the following issues were raised as either contributory factors or failures that should be highlighted:

- The company SMS procedures and industry best practices were not followed during the tank entry

- the Chief Officer had served with the company for nearly two years and was familiar with the company's SMS. Although the Master was new to the company, he had also been provided with familiarisation at the company's head offices. Both the Master and Chief Officer failed to follow the requirements of the company SMS

- the Chief Officer had also completed the required company SMS familiarisation programme onboard the vessel. However, this was not verified by the Master

- a permit to work was not raised. It was later ascertained that the Chief Officer had completed at least 15 tank entries during his time onboard. No permits were raised on any of these previous occasions. Complacency can be considered a major factor in the incident and the permit to work system was not effective

- the Master had assumed the Chief Officer's competence and adherence to company SMS requirements

- a company internal audit had previously raised a non-conformity with regard to non-compliance with the permit to work system. The non-conformity had been closed out by the Master. However, there was no evidence to confirm that effective action had been taken

- the tank entry was not identified as a working at height task. The Chief Officer was not, as a result of this oversight, wearing an appropriate fall arrester or working at height harness

- no portable lighting was put in place and the Chief Officer relied on a hand torch

- contingency arrangements were not put in place to deal with a rescue operation

- after the alarm was raised, at least 9 further crew members entered the tank without breathing apparatus or working at height harnesses. Although it was surmised that the Chief Officer had slipped and the tank atmosphere was not suspect, this could have resulted in further fatalities if the crew had made the wrong assessment of the cause of the accident

- rescue drills were required to be carried out onboard every 2 months, in compliance with the Entry into Dangerous Spaces (EDS) Regulations. These had not been completed. Had they been conducted, the need for rescue equipment at the tank entrance would have been highlighted and the crew may have been better prepared and organised for the rescue attempt.

9 Risk Assessments

Introduction

The use of the formal written risk assessment to identify and then control potential hazards is used to ensure the safety of all personnel conducting work onboard and to minimise accidents and ill health. The risk assessment process can be used for a variety of tasks and should be used to reduce risk levels to 'as low as reasonably practicable'. (ALARP)

Figure 9.1
Risk assessments can be used for a variety of work activities, including hot work

9.1 Regulations and Guidance

The HASW Regulations require all employers to evaluate the risks to which their employees may be exposed. In addition, the risk assessment process should consider the effects of the work activity on any persons onboard.

Risk	Risk is the chance that somebody will be harmed by a hazard
Hazard	A hazard is anything that can cause harm
Consequence	The harm that arises from a hazard

9.2 Principles of Risk Assessment

The content and scope of a risk assessment will depend on the nature and location of the work activity and the systems and personnel involved. However, some principles remain constant for any risk assessment:

- Risk assessment should be a core part of the SMS. The process should not be over-complicated

- all personnel should be provided with training in the use of the risk assessment process

- the risk assessment process should be conducted by personnel familiar with the proposed work scope, work area and who are involved in the proposed work activity

- all personnel conducting the work activity must be made aware of the identified hazards and the control measures

- all potential hazards should be assessed and control measures put in place and recorded

- the risk assessment should be a continuous process and should consider any changes in the work scope, equipment, personnel or working environment

- risk assessments for routine work activities must be reviewed prior to each work activity.

Figure 9.2
Mooring operations should be risk assessed

Where a risk assessment has previously been put in place for a particular work activity, it must be reviewed prior to commencement of the work. The existence of a risk assessment from previous operations does not negate the need for a further review.

9.3   Risk Assessment Methodology

The risk assessment methodology should be simple and easy to understand and described in the SMS.

1.   Classify work activities

2.   Identify hazards

3.   Identify risk controls

4.   Estimate risk

5.   Determine tolerability of risk

6.   Risk control

7.   Work activity

8.   Review.

Step 1 – Classify Work Activities

The type of work to be conducted, the work location and the scheduled duration of the work should be identified and consideration should be given to the impact on any other work activities or personnel onboard.

Step 2 – Identify Hazards

Consideration should be given to the physical aspects of the work and system hazards. It is essential that the worksite is inspected and that manufacturers' and industry information and guidance is consulted.

Physical Hazards	
Hazard	*Example*
Access and egress	*Poor access and egress arrangements can introduce slip, trip and fall hazards*
Chemical	*Exposure to chemicals or other substances*
Dropped objects	*Work activities above areas where other personnel may be working may introduce dropped object hazards*
Electrical	*Contact with un-isolated fixed or portable electrical equipment*
Enclosed space	*Restricted movement and exposure to atmospheres deficient in oxygen or liable to contain flammable or toxic gases may be introduced*

Environmental	Weather conditions such as ice accretion can introduce slip, trip and fall hazards
Equipment	Equipment that has been poorly maintained could fail, causing injury
Lighting	Low lighting levels might introduce slip, trip or fall hazards
Manual handling	Injury to personnel due to failure to train personnel in safe techniques
Mechanical	Contact with moving parts or machinery
Noise	Exposure to excessive noise levels from fixed or portable machinery
Pressure	Failure of equipment, lack of isolation or failure of protection devices resulting in the release of stored pressure
Radiation	Exposure to radiation due to poor storage of substances
Simultaneous operations	Bunkering operations being conducted at the same time as hot work
Spills	Poor storage or handling of chemicals or other substances can result in spills
Thermal	Exposure or contact with extremes of temperature
Tools	The use of the incorrect or inadequate tools can introduce hazards liable to cause injury
Vibration	Vibration can introduce health hazards such as hand arm vibration syndrome (white finger)
Work at height	Work aloft or overside will expose fall hazards

System Hazards	
Hazard	**Example**
Design	Failure of equipment due to poor design for the intended use
Procedures	Poor, inadequate, uncontrolled or unapproved procedures can result in incorrect or inadequate control measures
Information	A lack of information on equipment or substances being used can lead to improper use and unforeseen hazards
Planning	Inadequate planning may fail to consider equipment limitations
Communications	Poor communication can result in accidents or injuries
Personnel	Inadequate resources in the form of personnel can lead to time pressures on personnel
Supervision	Insufficient supervision can result in personnel failing to follow defined procedures and systems
Training	Failure to provide suitable training can lead to incorrect use of equipment

Table 9.1
Hazard identification

Step 3 – Identify Risk Controls

Once all potential hazards have been identified and a thorough review and inspection has been conducted at the worksite, the risk assessment methodology should identify the control measures that can be implemented to reduce or eliminate the risks. A structured risk control hierarchy should be used to eliminate, substitute or reduce the hazards.

Eliminate	Remove or eliminate the potential hazard completely. It may be that the work activity can be cancelled
Substitute	It may be possible to use alternative work methods, use different procedures or use different equipment, materials or tools
Reduce	Reduce the potential exposure to the hazard by reducing the numbers of personnel involved, the quantities of chemicals or substances or by reducing the exposure time
Barriers	It may be possible to use barriers or guards to reduce exposure to risk
Engineering Controls	It may be possible to reduce the risk by the use of warning systems, alarms, other equipment or systems or other engineering controls
Personal Protective Equipment	PPE should only be utilised as a control measure after all other control measures have been considered

Table 9.2
Risk control hierarchy

Figure 9.3
Non-routine operations and specialised activities should be subject to risk assessment

Step 4 – Estimate Risk

The estimation of the severity of harm to an individual from a potential hazard is difficult to quantify. In estimating severity, the type of injury and the location on the body where the injury could be received should be considered, along with the possible short-term and long-term health impact on the individual.

The likelihood of harm depends on the type of activity, the equipment and substances involved, the number of personnel involved in the work activity and the duration of the exposure to the hazard.

Likelihood of Harm	Severity of Harm		
	Slight (I)	Moderate (II)	Extreme (III)
Very Unlikely (A)	VERY LOW RISK	VERY LOW RISK	HIGH RISK
Unlikely (B)	VERY LOW RISK	MEDIUM RISK	VERY HIGH RISK
Likely (C)	LOW RISK	HIGH RISK	VERY HIGH RISK
Very Likely (D)	LOW RISK	VERY HIGH RISK	VERY HIGH RISK

Table 9.3
Example risk estimation table

Step 5 – Determine Tolerability of Risk

Once the risk and its potential severity is identified, personnel involved in the proposed work activity should determine whether the risks are acceptable or unacceptable.

Step 6 – Risk Control

The final step prior to commencement of the work activity requires the introduction of risk control measures and a revision of the risk estimation.

A review of the risk control measures already in place should be conducted prior to considering the introduction of further controls.

All identified control measures should be documented and agreed by all personnel involved in the risk assessment process.

Recommendations or actions agreed at this stage should be appropriate for the task and it should be practical to implement them.

The residual risk, taking into consideration the implemented control measures, should be ALARP.

A tool box talk prior to commencing the work is an appropriate added control to ensure that all personnel are aware of the hazards, control measures and any residual risks.

Step 7 – Work Activity

During the work activity, it is essential that all personnel are aware that they have the authority to stop operations if at any time they feel the situation has changed and the work activity is now unsafe.

Step 8 – Review

Risk assessment is a continuous process and should be reviewed before the work activity starts and throughout its duration.

Changes to the working environment, working practices or changes to the actual work task are all valid reasons for reviewing the risk assessment and such reviews are an important aspect of the process.

On completion of the work activity, any lessons learned may also highlight a need to amend the risk assessment and the control measures.

The risk assessment process is in place to avoid incidents or accidents and to maintain the health and safety of all personnel. However, if the work activity leads to an incident or accident, it is important that lessons are learned and that these lessons are incorporated into any future risk assessments.

Example Risk Assessment – Mooring Operations

Work Activity	Hazard	Hazard Effect	Severity of Harm	Likelihood of Harm	Risk Rating	Control Measures	Revised Risk Rating	Actionee
Mooring operations	Failure of fixed or temporary mooring equipment	Injury to personnel and damage to equipment	III	B	Very high	Design control of fixed mooring equipment to industry standards Temporary mooring equipment purchased with due regard to fixed mooring equipment limitations Safe use of work equipment assessments Identification and highlighting of 'snap-back zones' Planned maintenance and regular inspections Familiarisation and training of mooring team with equipment limitations	LOW	C/O
	Slips, trips and falls	Injury to personnel	III	C	Very high	Anti-slip coating on all mooring station work areas Planned maintenance and regular inspections PPE	LOW	C/O
	Manual handling	Injury to personnel	II	C	High	Use of mechanical lifting devices Training in manual handling techniques	LOW	C/O
	Contact with moving machinery	Injury to personnel	III	B	Very high	Planned maintenance and regular inspections of guards and emergency stops Safe use of work equipment assessments PPE guards	LOW	C/O

10 Permit to Work Systems (PTW)

A PTW is a formal written system for controlling potentially hazardous work and activities onboard ship. The PTW system should be a key element in the SMS and should be used for activities where there is potential hazard to the health and safety of personnel. The PTW system can be used for simple tasks, eg planned maintenance activities and for more complex operations such as tank cleaning and entry into enclosed spaces.

Each shipping company will have its own PTW systems, which may change from ship to ship, depending on the ship type. It is, therefore, essential that all new crew are trained and familiarised in the specific PTW system and its application onboard.

Figure 10.1
Some permits are colour coded for ease of use

For ships that operate within the safety zones of offshore platforms and for ships that conduct operations in close proximity to other ships, the use of a PTW may be commonplace to control simultaneous activities on more than one ship.

Figure 10.2
PTW systems can be used to control activities between more than one ship or installation

10.1 Regulations and Guidance

The IMO provides guidance on the basic elements required of a health and safety programme. The use of a PTW system is suggested as one of the hazard control measures for lock out and tag out (electrical isolations), tank or hold cleaning operations, confined (enclosed) space entry, hot work and working at height (aloft).

Chapter 16 of the Code of Safe Working Practices for Merchant Seamen (COSWP) expands on the benefits and application of a PTW system as a hazard control measure.

IMO

Guidelines on the Basic Elements of a Shipboard Occupational Health and Safety Programme

http://shippingregs.org/34.re

10.2   Principles of the PTW System

A PTW system does not replace a risk assessment, which must always be conducted where activities are planned that may pose a potential hazard.

Figure 10.3
Bunkering operations should be controlled by use of a permit to work

The risk assessment process will, if conducted correctly, identify the requirements, and the need for work to be conducted under the control of a PTW.

Activities that would usually require a PTW include:

- Hot work including burning, grinding and welding

- working at height and overside operations

- work on electrical equipment and installations

- work on mechanical equipment and installations

- entry into enclosed spaces

- tank cleaning operations

- bunkering operations

- heavy lift operations

- simultaneous operations.

The main purpose of any PTW system is to ensure that the safety of all personnel involved in the work and all those onboard is maintained at all times. This is achieved by ensuring that all potential hazards have been identified, considered and controlled prior to commencement of the work activity.

The use of a PTW does not ensure that all risks and hazards have been eliminated from the proposed work activity and does not indicate that the work is now considered safe. The PTW is a control measure.

The PTW system must:

- Be documented as part of the ship's SMS

- comply with all relevant international, national and company standards, rules and regulations

- identify the key personnel onboard required to authorise work activities, electrical and mechanical isolations and to issue permits

- define the duties and responsibilities of those personnel tasked with the authorisation or issue of permits

- ensure that all personnel required to authorise or issue permits and all personnel required to operate within the controls of a PTW system are suitably familiarised and trained in its use

- define the routine and non-routine activities where a permit to work must be utilised

- identify the hazards associated with the routine or non-routine activity, the work location and any other simultaneous operations

- have inspected the proposed work site as part of the PTW process. The site inspection should be conducted by personnel familiar with the area and the equipment and systems within that area. Personnel designated to conduct site inspections must be competent to do so

- consider communication at all times. The PTW must be used to ensure that all personnel who are involved in the proposed work activity, or may be affected by the work activity, are advised of the activity.

Maritime and Coastguard Agency

Code of Safe Working Practices for Merchant Seamen (COSWP) Chapter 16

http://shippingregs.org/14.re

10.3   PTW System

All PTW systems will be different and specific to the company or ship. The following is an example methodology:

1. SMS

2. Risk assessment

3. Authorised personnel

4. Communication and coordination

5. The permit

6. The work activity

7. Auditing and review.

Step 1 – Safety Management System

The SMS, as per the ISM Code, requires shipping companies to develop a safe system of work for shipboard operations, including the provision of a PTW system.

Figure 10.4
A permit to work system can be used to control electrical isolations

Step 2 – Risk Assessment

A risk assessment, as described in Chapter 9, must be completed prior to the issue of a PTW. The risk assessment will identify any potential hazards associated with the work activity and will identify the control measures required prior to commencement of the work. The PTW is one of the control measures.

Step 3 – Authorised Personnel

The PTW system should be controlled and coordinated from one location. Generally, this will be the bridge, but there may be certain ships where a more suitable location is used or where more than one control station is utilised. This may be acceptable in certain circumstances, but it must always be remembered that one of the key purposes of the PTW system is to ensure that work activities are coordinated between all personnel and all departments onboard.

Personnel responsible for issuing permits, inspecting the work area prior to issue, in charge of any work being conducted under the control of a permit and responsible for auditing the permit system must be trained and competent in its use. An organisation chart can help ensure clarity of roles and responsibilities.

It is often not possible for those responsible for issuing and coordinating the PTW system to visually inspect the worksite. It is a common practice for persons to be nominated as permit authorities for specific areas onboard the ship. For example, the Chief Engineer or his deputy may be nominated as the area authority for the engine room and machinery spaces and the Chief Officer for the main deck and accommodation areas. By nominating area authorities, the worksite can be inspected and checks made regarding the proposed work activity and control measures, by person(s) with intimate knowledge of the work area and of activities within the work area. In addition, these personnel should have the competence to review the potential hazards and the proposed work scope.

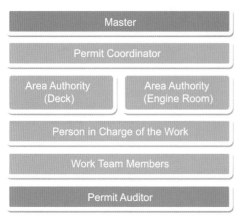

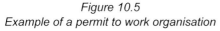

Figure 10.5
Example of a permit to work organisation

Step 4 – Communication and Coordination

Communication ensures that all relevant personnel are aware of ongoing work activities and this should help prevent dangerous situations occuring, due to simultaneous operations.

Communication and coordination is also essential between the personnel inspecting the work site, conducting the work and issuing the permit to work.

Step 5 – The Permit

The permit should:

- Describe the proposed work activity in detail, including a thorough description of the work activity, its location, the estimated duration, and the persons performing it. Any equipment that will be used should be identified

- state the control measures that have been put in place to reduce or eliminate the hazards associated

with the work. For example, if a fire watch is required during hot work, then this control measure should be identified on the permit

- identify mechanical or electrical isolations to be put in place as a control measure. The precise details of the isolation should be recorded to ensure that the isolation can be confirmed and that there is no possibility that it can be removed

- allow for a review and sign off during the work activity. This will ensure that no work is conducted without the prior authorisation of the area authority and the permit coordinator.

Procedures should clearly indicate where the permit should be displayed. Generally, this should include the permit control station and the worksite as a minimum.

Step 6 – The Work Activity

The risk assessment and PTW processes do not stop once the work activity commences.

At all stages, any changes to the potential hazards must be considered. This may include residual risks from the work activity, such as paint fumes, and any environmental changes, such as the effects of the weather.

The control measures put in place prior to the commencement of the work activity should remain in place until all the work has been completed.

In circumstances where changes to the work activity, the environment or simultaneous operations may affect safety, the PTW should be suspended and the work activity re-assessed prior to re-commencement.

Step 7 – Auditing and Review

Internal audits as required by the ISM Code, should include a review of the PTW system and isolation requirements.

AUTHOR'S NOTE The PTW system is so crucial to everyday operations that it is advisable that more regular audits are conducted.

Regular monitoring and auditing ensures that standards are maintained.

A simple auditing method is to conduct random spot checks of the permit to work system, which should include a review of the available documentation. The information detailed in the PTW should be reviewed and checked to ensure that the appropriate measures have been taken to control the proposed work activity.

Checks should be made to ensure that the personnel involved are trained and competent to fulfil their roles and that all personnel required to work within the permit system are aware of their roles and responsibilities.

Any control measures highlighted during the risk assessment process should be checked and the worksite inspected. Where additional safety precautions or control measures such as barriers, extra fire-fighting equipment or specific PPE are required to be put in place, these should be verified visually.

Figure 10.6
Visual checks should be made as part of the audit process

Where the PTW relates to electrical or mechanical isolations, an auditor can verify that company requirements and good practices have been followed to ensure that the isolation is suitable and sufficient.

Case Study: *'Piper Alpha'*

'Piper Alpha' was originally an oil production platform built in 1975 for Occidental Petroleum Limited. Located 120 nautical miles North East of Aberdeen, Scotland, the platform consisted of 4 separate modules and had been designed so that the living accommodation was separate and segregated from the operational areas.

Oil production from *'Piper Alpha'* commenced in 1976 and the platform was later converted for gas production. This conversion required a number of changes to the layout of the platform and resulted in several key or critical areas (such as the platform control room) being located close to operational areas.

Incident Summary

The *'Piper Alpha'* tragedy occurred on 6th July 1988. A total of 167 died in the incident, including 2 crew from the standby vessel *'Sandhaven'*. The *'Sandhaven'* was one of the vessels engaged in the ensuing rescue operations in which 59 men were rescued.

The following text is a summary of events to highlight the importance of PTW systems. It is not a full and in-depth narrative or a full review of all the failures that led to the disaster.

The ignition point for the initial explosion and resulting fire was one of the platform's two condensate pumps (designated pump 'A' and 'B'). The purpose of these pumps was to compress the gas prior to pumping ashore.

During 6th July, routine maintenance was being carried out on a pressure safety valve on pump 'A', which required the condensate pipework to be blanked off.

The routine maintenance could not be completed during the working shift of the personnel involved and the pipework remained blanked off at the end of the shift. The PTW was filed with the control room with details of the status of pump 'A'. The status of the pump was not relayed to the oncoming night duty when the control room shift change took place at 18:00 hrs.

A few hours later at approximately 21:45 hrs, condensate pump 'B' stopped unexpectedly and could not be re-started.

None of those on duty were aware of the PTW that was in place for the condensate pump routine maintenance and were unaware that the pipe work was blanked off and the pump was out of service. After attempts to re-start pump 'B' failed, the decision was made to start the out of service pump 'A' to maintain production.

Pump 'A' was started at 21:55 hrs. Gas flowed into the pump and, with the safety valve temporarily removed, overpressure blew off the temporary blank. The effects were almost immediate with the escaping gas igniting and an explosion rocking the platform.

The control room was abandoned within minutes of this initial explosion and as fire quickly spread, the lack of a central control point was to prove critical. Those onboard were unable to muster at their lifeboat stations, due to the intensity of the fires, and were forced into the accommodation block. The majority waited in this area for helicopter evacuation. However, the helideck was engulfed in flames and smoke and there was no chance of rescue by this means.

At the time of the incident, the *'Piper Alpha'* fire-fighting systems were all on manual control. This was a routine occurrence when divers were deployed. There was, therefore, no opportunity for the crew to attempt to control the fire, although attempts were made to start the fire-fighting pumps manually.

Added to this, the fire on *'Piper Alpha'* was being fuelled by oil being pumped from the connected *'Tartan'* and *'Claymore'* platforms. Both platforms continued to pump oil to *'Piper Alpha'* after the initial explosion.

At approximately 22:50 hrs, a second explosion engulfed the platform, at which point *'Claymore'* finally stopped pumping. Within an hour the accommodation block had collapsed into the sea and by 00:45 hrs on 7th July, the majority of the platform was destroyed.

Incident Investigation

The public inquiry into the disaster was one of the most thorough and detailed ever carried out in any industry. A total of 48 recommendations were made as a result. Of these recommendations, the need for the provision of suitably designed, constructed and equipped dedicated standby vessels was a major finding and was to have a far reaching impact in the oil and gas industry.

In addition to these standby vessel specific requirements, the key recommendation of the Lord Cullen Report was the instigation of mandatory Safety Cases for every installation in the UK Continental Shelf.

The Safety Case, which has to be submitted and accepted by the Health and Safety Executive (HSE), would be used to document and demonstrate the

Figure 10.7
'Piper Alpha' Memorial

provision of a suitable and sufficient SMS, emergency and evacuation plans, procedures and risk controls for all operations and the provision of a temporary refuge during emergencies. The need for a suitable and sufficient PTW system was a key element in these requirements.

 Public Inquiry into the Piper Alpha Disaster

http://shippingregs.org/35.re

11 Entry into Enclosed Spaces

Entry into enclosed spaces is one of the most hazardous activities undertaken onboard any vessel type and there have been many instances where multiple loss of life has resulted from failures in procedures. The hazardous nature of such activities have been compounded by failures to correctly identify what constitutes an enclosed space. Multiple loss of life is often the result of failed rescue attempts to save colleagues in distress.

 Terms such as 'confined space', 'enclosed space' and 'dangerous space' are used in the guidance available, but for the purposes of clarity, the term 'enclosed space' will be used throughout this section.

11.1 Regulations and Guidance

The IMO Resolution A.864 (20) 'Recommendations for Entering Enclosed Spaces Aboard Ships' is central to all regulations and guidance and they encourage the adoption of safety procedures aimed at preventing further casualties in enclosed spaces with an oxygen-deficient, toxic or flammable atmosphere.

Flag State Authorities have put in place their own specific requirements. For example, the UK's Merchant Shipping (Entry into Dangerous Spaces) Regulations apply to all UK registered vessels and all vessels when operating in a UK port.

The Code of Safe Working Practices for Merchant Seamen (COSWP), Chapter 17 (Entering Enclosed or Confined Spaces) also contains valuable information and guidance.

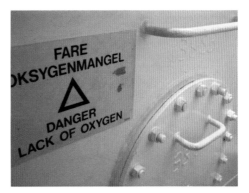

Figure 11.1
Recommended practices should be followed for all enclosed space entry operations

11.2 Enclosed Spaces

The IMO defines 'enclosed space' as a space that has any of the following characteristics:

- Limited openings for entry and exit

- unfavourable natural ventilation

- is not designed for continuous worker occupancy.

The main spaces on a ship that the majority would associate with the term 'enclosed space' are fuel or liquid cargo tanks. However, the number and variety of spaces that can be described as such, and which pose potential hazards to personnel, is extensive, as highlighed by Table 11.1.

Fuel Tanks	Ballast Tanks
Fresh Water Tanks	Cargo Tanks
Cargo Holds	Stability Tanks
Chain Lockers	Void Spaces
Cofferdams	Duct Keels
Pump Rooms	Sewage Tanks
Crankcases	Equipment Spaces
Battery Lockers	Spaces through which hold ventilation runs
Cargo Hold Stairways	Store Rooms

Table 11.1
Enclosed spaces

Figure 11.2
Crane housings can be considered enclosed spaces

11.3 Enclosed Space Hazards

It can be necessary to enter enclosed spaces for:

- Routine planned maintenance

- cargo cleaning operations

- inspections, surveys

- repair work etc.

The general hazards associated with entry into an enclosed space to perform any of these tasks will depend on the type of space and the nature of substances carried within it. However, there are some general hazards that are applicable in most circumstances:

- Access, lighting and general hazards

- oxygen deficient atmosphere

- toxic atmosphere

- flammable atmosphere.

Access, Lighting and General Hazards

Tank manhole covers may be located in easily accessible places on deck, but may be situated in locations that are hard to access, such as under engine room deck plates. They may also be obstructed by pipe work or machinery.

Consideration must, therefore, be given at the planning stage as to how the manhole cover will be removed and how it will subsequently be replaced. Personnel entering the tank will need a safe means of access. The options for rescuing an incapacitated crew member will also need to be considered.

If the external access and the access within the enclosed space is through a fixed vertical ladder, its condition should be checked before entry. Corrosion within tanks can cause considerable deterioration, particularly at securing points of the access way and these should be checked.

Cargo residues, oil or rust scale within an enclosed space can greatly increase the potential for slips, trips and falls and attention should be paid to residues on access ladders and internal walkways and platforms.

Depending on the nature of the enclosed space, the work to be conducted may also be considered as work at height.

Intrinsically safe portable lighting will be needed at the access points and within the enclosed space to ensure that adequate lighting is available in all work areas.

Oxygen Deficient Atmosphere

Any atmosphere less than 20.8% oxygen by volume should not be entered.

An oxygen deficient atmosphere can occur:

- In an enclosed space, such as a cargo tank or hold, where

oxygen depleting or self-heating cargoes are being carried or have previously been carried. This may include cargoes of grain, timber products, iron, metals, vegetables and wood pellets

- through the rusting process in tanks, particularly ballast tanks

- in circumstances where work within an enclosed space, such as burning, welding or painting has recently been performed

- in circumstances where a fire extinguishing agent, such as CO_2, has been released into a cargo tank, hold or engine room

- where fumigation has been conducted.

Asphyxiation is the deprivation of oxygen caused by the presence of a contaminant in the air or a mechanical obstruction to breathing.

Toxic Atmosphere

Toxins are measured in parts per million (ppm) - under no circumstances should anyone enter an enclosed space exceeding the specified limits.

A toxic atmosphere can pose serious hazards to the health of personnel onboard ship, particularly when toxic gases are inhaled or are absorbed through contact with the skin or ingestion.

A toxic atmosphere can be present:

- In a cargo tank or hold where toxic substances are carried or have been carried as cargo. This will be most evident on chemical and oil tankers, but may also be applicable on general cargo ships and bulk carriers carrying cargoes such as grain. Disturbing cargo residues may result in the release of toxic gases

- in tanks where toxic substances have previously been carried, but where the tanks have remained unused for some time. In such circumstances, the disturbance of rust or scale may result in the release of toxic gases

- in tanks that have previously contained crude oil or its products, hydrocarbon gases may be present

- in spaces adjacent to tanks and holds. Special consideration should be given to all pump rooms, cofferdams and void spaces adjacent to or connected to cargo tanks and holds

- in holds or other spaces where hazardous cargoes are carried in packaged form as there may be leakage

- in the presence of water as, while some substances may not be inherently toxic, they may release toxic gases when mixed with water

- where inert gas systems that contain trace components that are hazardous are used

- after certain types of work within enclosed spaces, including grit blasting, painting, cleaning or hot work. This may be as a result of the process, the chemicals used or the interaction between the substances used and the tank coatings or residues within the space.

Flammable Atmosphere

> **A space with an atmosphere with more than 1% of the 'lower flammable limit' (LFL) or 'lower explosive limit' (LEL) on a combustible gas indicator should not be entered**

11.4 Enclosed Space Entry Methodology

The methodology should be clearly defined in the company's SMS and should identify the process for assessing enclosed space entry risks, control measures available, enclosed space entry precautions and contingency procedures. These include:

1. Safety Management System

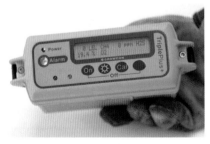

Figure 11.3
Gas detector showing 0% LEL, 0ppm H₂S and 19.4% O₂. While there is 0% LEL, the O₂ level is less than 20.8% and therefore unsafe to enter (Note this O₂ reading of 19.4% was achieved by exhaling on the sensor)

2. Assess the risk

3. Control measures

4. Precautions during entry

5. Contingency arrangements.

The methodology should:

- Provide for enclosed space entry only where there is no other alternative

- ensure that all personnel required to enter enclosed spaces or provide assistance in normal or emergency situations are provided with adequate and appropriate levels of training

- ensure that all associated processes within the SMS, including the PTW system and risk assessment tools, are followed

- identify the potential hazards associated with the particular space and proposed task

- ensure that information is available regarding previous cargoes and substances carried in the enclosed space. For example, for gas carriers, a data sheet for the last cargo should be available and for chemical tankers, a data sheet for the previous three cargoes should be available

- ensure that all additional requirements and precautions are taken for specific cargoes and vessel types. For example, entry procedures for enclosed spaces adjacent to loaded tanks on double-hull tankers, require additional

precautions and a two stage entry procedure

- ensure that all identified hazards are assessed and control measures put in place to mitigate against the potential effects

- ensure that all necessary steps are taken to thoroughly ventilate the enclosed space by all available means

- ensure that the atmosphere of the enclosed space is thoroughly tested, at all levels, with suitable and appropriate calibrated equipment, to ascertain the oxygen content and potential toxic or flammable atmospheres

- ensure that access to enclosed spaces is suitable for safe entry and for safe exit during normal operations and in emergency situations where rescue plans may be put into action

- ensure that access to enclosed spaces is secure when unattended, to ensure that unauthorised personnel cannot access the space inadvertently or intentionally

- ensure that all personnel engaged in enclosed space entry operations are provided with the correct PPE that is appropriate for the space and task to be performed

- ensure that a system of communication is agreed and adhered to prior to and during all enclosed space entry procedures

- ensure that a suitably competent and knowledgeable standby person is assigned to maintain a watch at the enclosed space entry access, at all times where persons may be within the space

- ensure that appropriate emergency and rescue equipment is available and in good working order at the access points

- ensure that routine drills are conducted onboard for normal enclosed space entry tasks so that personnel are familiar with the equipment, methodology and rescue scenarios.

Maritime and Coastguard Agency

MGN 423(M)
Entry into Dangerous Spaces

http://shippingregs.org/36.re

International Maritime Organization

Resolution A.864(20)
Recommendations for Entering Enclosed Spaces Aboard Ships

http://shippingregs.org/37.re

11.4.1 *Safety Management System*

- Training and drills

- procedures

- permit to work system.

Step 1.1 – Training and Drills

All personnel responsible for the implementation of enclosed space entry procedures and those involved in work within enclosed spaces onboard the ship should be provided with training.

Masters and officers responsible for the management of the enclosed space entry operations must be provided with training in the fundamentals of enclosed spaces, the associated dangers and the precautions to be taken prior to, during and on completion of enclosed space entry. Particular emphasis should be placed on potential hazards such as oxygen depleted, toxic and flammable atmospheres and the testing equipment that is in use onboard.

Training and familiarisation in the use of all equipment, including rescue equipment, should form part of the vessel's routine drills schedule. Drills simulating the rescue of a crew member from an enclosed space should be conducted every two months. Such drills should also be used for simulation of tank entry procedures where there is no actual emergency so that personnel become familiarised with the correct methodology and process.

Step 1.2 – Procedures

The ISM Code requires all shipping companies to have procedures for critical operations. Entry into enclosed spaces should be considered as a critical operation and detailed procedures should be in place for the planning, execution of work within and safe exit from such spaces.

The procedures should identify the potential enclosed spaces on the vessel and the potential activities and cargoes that may pose a hazard. The procedures should specify the methodology and tasks to be completed during the preparation for entry, during entry and for contingency purposes.

The procedures should identify who is responsible for ensuring that the procedures are followed (the Master) and for safe entry (usually the Chief Officer). In addition, training requirements and the equipment to be held onboard and used during entry tasks, training drills and for contingencies, should be specified.

Step 1.3 – Permit to Work System

The PTW system should form an integral part of the entry into enclosed space procedures and should be used in all such circumstances. The PTW system should control and coordinate activities, ensuring that all relevant personnel are aware of the ongoing entry tasks and ensure that any simultaneous operations onboard do not pose a potential hazard to the personnel conducting the entry procedures.

The issue of a PTW in respect of the enclosed space entry should be used as a check to confirm that all pre-entry checks, including atmosphere testing, have been adequately completed and that all potential risks have been identified, assessed and reviewed.

11.4.2 *Assess the Risk*

- Responsibilities

- identify and assess potential hazards.

Step 2.1 – Responsibilities

The Master is responsible for the health and safety of all personnel onboard any vessel and has the overall responsibility for ensuring that all entry into enclosed space operations are conducted in accordance with the IMO recommendations, company requirements and good safe working practices.

However, it is acceptable for a responsible officer to be delegated to oversee enclosed space entries. The designated officer, as a responsible and competent person, will be responsible for ensuring that the company procedures are adhered to, that the permit to work system is followed, that all potential risks are identified and assessed and will be responsible for monitoring all control measures until the safe completion of the task.

The responsible officer must be suitably trained and must have both theoretical and practical knowledge and experience of entry into enclosed space procedures. It is essential that this officer has awareness of all aspects of such operations, particularly the potential hazards associated with enclosed spaces and flammable, toxic and oxygen deficient atmospheres.

Figure 11.4
Competent personnel should assess the risks

Step 2.2 – Identify and Assess Potential Hazards

There should be a thorough review of the proposed task to identify all potential hazards, which should include all personnel directly involved with the proposed task.

Consideration should be given to previous and current cargoes and residues (toxicity, flammability and oxygen depletion properties), previous and current substances (chemicals, ballast water), means of access and egress, position of the space (for rescues), ventilation available and any other pertinent information.

The identification of all potential hazards for the enclosed space entry will allow the responsible officer and crew members to assess the risks to personnel and will help define the control measures that will be required to allow the entry to go ahead in a safe and controlled manner.

11.4.3   *Control Measures*

- Authorisation

- coordination and communication

- means of access

- isolation

- ventilation

- measuring devices

- testing the atmosphere.

Step 3.1 – Authorisation

It should be a standing order that no person should enter a designated enclosed space without the express approval of the vessel's Master or a designated person nominated by them. This is the most basic high-level control measure and should ensure that the Master is aware of all enclosed space activities onboard the vessel.

Step 3.2 – Coordination and Communication

Good communications between the personnel working in the enclosed space and the standby personnel, and between the standby personnel and the bridge and PTW coordinator, is crucial.

Prior to entry, a communication system should be established between all parties to ensure that the standby personnel, bridge or the PTW coordinator can be made immediately aware of any problems within the enclosed space.

Figure 11.5
Enclosed space entry tasks should be controlled and good communication maintained with the Officer of the Watch

Step 3.3 – Means of Access

Access and egress from the space should be considered for both the entry procedure and for any contingency situations.

In the first instance, it is essential that the correct means of access is identified. In the case of tank lids, the failure to correctly identify the correct access may result in serious consequences. The responsible officer must ensure that the correct tank lid is identified and should confirm that the space has been emptied and that the space is not pressurised.

Access and egress routes should be unobstructed, well illuminated and free from any potential hazards such as spillages. The access ladders, hand holds and steps should all be in good condition.

The location and dimensions of the access and egress should allow personnel to enter while wearing breathing apparatus and other forms of PPE in the event of a rescue operation.

Figure 11.7
Some access points may pose
additional hazards

Means of Access

All entrances to unattended enclosed spaces on the ship should be either kept closed and/or secured.

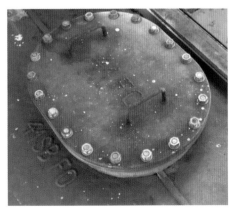

Figure 11.6
Some access points may be easily
accessible

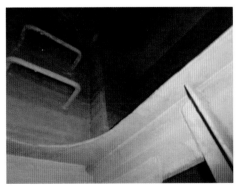

Figure 11.8
Internal access ways may be unprotected
and residues can pose hazards

Step 3.4 – Isolations

If the enclosed space to be entered is a cargo tank, fuel oil tank, ballast tank or other compartment where a substance may be inadvertently pumped into the space, appropriate mechanical isolations should be put in place. These may include the securing of pumps and the securing or blanking of valves. In addition, notices should be posted at all relevant control stations (cargo or ballast panels) and the bridge and PTW coordinator should be informed. Any mechanical isolation in place should be clearly noted on the PTW.

It may be necessary to electrically isolate equipment prior to entry into a space. All electrical isolations should be suitably marked and the bridge and PTW coordinator advised. Any electrical isolation should be clearly noted on the PTW.

Step 3.5 – Ventilation

Prior to entry into any enclosed space, suitable natural or mechanical ventilation must take place, the extent of which will depend on the nature of the cargoes, substances and any residues in the space.

The nature of the previous contents of the tank should not negate the use of ventilation.

If natural ventilation is used, it is preferable that a second entry point is opened to allow for free flow of air through the enclosed space.

Ventilation should continue during all entry operations, during the period that the enclosed space is occupied and during any breaks in the tasks. If the mechanical ventilation fails or the natural ventilation is in some way obstructed, all personnel should exit the enclosed space until the situation can be rectified.

Pure or compressed oxygen should never be used to ventilate an enclosed space.

Step 3.6 – Measuring Devices

Measuring devices for testing toxic, flammable and oxygen deficient atmospheres should be provided onboard all vessels where there is the potential for such hazards to exist. Any measuring devices provided should be in good working order, regularly serviced and calibrated in accordance with the manufacturer's instructions.

Figure 11.9
GX-2009 Multi-Gas Detector

The Maritime and Coastguard Agency strongly advises that all ships over 24 metres in length, and smaller vessels that have enclosed spaces that seafarers are likely to enter, should carry an oxygen meter onboard at all times.

Figure 11.10
GX-2009 Multi-Gas Detector with hand aspirator

Step 3.7 – Testing the Atmosphere

The testing process will be used to confirm the hazards and to measure the effectiveness of any control measures (such as ventilation).

- Testing of the atmosphere should be conducted by trained personnel using calibrated measuring devices

- the measuring devices should be appropriate for the potential hazards. For example, using an oxygen meter in a potentially toxic atmosphere will not provide any indication of the presence of toxic vapours

- personal monitors are not designed to be used for the testing of an enclosed space atmosphere, but are provided as a personal alarm. Only measuring devices specifically designed for testing operations should be used

- testing of the atmosphere should be conducted at as many levels of the enclosed space as is practicable. It should be considered that the gases within the space may be heavier or lighter than air and so pockets of gas may be present

- any mechanical ventilation should be stopped during the testing process to ensure that an accurate reading of the enclosed space atmosphere can be obtained

- testing of the atmosphere should be conducted prior to entry and at regular intervals during the entry operations. If operations are suspended for any reason, then testing should be conducted again before re-entry

- personnel should avoid entering the space to perform testing. If this cannot be avoided, breathing apparatus should be worn and all rescue equipment and personnel must be in place. If there is deterioration in the atmosphere, all personnel must leave the space immediately

Figure 11.11
Testing should include all areas of the
enclosed space

- in circumstances where an enclosed space has previously been tested and found safe, testing should still be conducted. No personnel should ever assume the atmosphere within an enclosed space is safe

Oxygen limits should not be less than 20.8% by volume and not more than 1% of the lower flammable limit (LFL). Readings for toxic gases or vapours should be below occupational exposure limits

- if safe levels are not recorded, personnel should refrain from entering the enclosed space until further ventilation and subsequent testing can be conducted.

Figure 11.12
GX-2009 Multi-Gas Detector with hand aspirated sample draw and probe for remote testing

Multi-gas detectors can be used to detect areas of oxygen deficiency and elevated levels of oxygen, combustible gases, carbon monoxide and hydrogen sulphide.

11.4.4 *Precautions during Entry*

- Standby Person

- limit exposure

- continuous ventilation

- continuous monitoring.

Step 4.1 – Standby Person

No person should ever enter an enclosed space without there being a standby person assigned at the entrance to the space. The standby person should be properly trained and aware that their sole function is to raise the alarm under any circumstances where the safety of personnel within the space may be compromised. The standby person must not, therefore, be given any other duties, must remain at the entry point at all times and must maintain communication lines with the bridge at all times. The standby person must be made aware of the dangers of entering an enclosed space to effect a rescue and must not, under any circumstances, enter the space.

Step 4.2 – Limit Exposure

If an enclosed space entry is unavoidable, an effective control measure is to limit the number of personnel exposed to the potential hazards and the time that they are within the enclosed space. The number of personnel should be limited to only those necessary to conduct the proposed tasks in a safe and controlled manner. Pre-planning of the tasks will also ensure that the time spent within the space is limited.

Step 4.3 – Continuous Ventilation

The atmosphere within an enclosed space can change over a period of time and continuous ventilation of the space should be maintained. For example, personnel entering an enclosed space may disturb residues, releasing toxic or flammable gases.

Step 4.4 – Continuous Monitoring

Monitoring of the atmosphere of any enclosed space must be continued regularly during all stages of the task. Any changes to the atmosphere must be communicated to all parties and operations should be suspended if there are any doubts about the atmospheric conditions. Personnel should exit the space in such circumstances.

11.4.5   Contingency Arrangements

- Awareness

- contingency plans

- contingency equipment.

Step 5.1 – Awareness

Crew members must be aware of the actions to be taken in an emergency situation. In particular, personnel tasked with standby duties, and the bridge officer will be the first aware of an emergency situation and so they must be adequately trained in their duties.

AUTHOR'S NOTE

All personnel must be aware that they should NEVER enter an enclosed space to attempt a rescue operation until the alarm has been raised and all preparations made to ensure their own safety.

Step 5.2 – Contingency Plans

Specific contingency plans for rescue should be in place and they should take into account the type and location of the space and the personnel and equipment available to conduct any rescue operation.

Crew must also be provided with training and drills for enclosed space rescues, which should ensure they are familiar and trained in the actions to be taken and the rescue equipment available (including breathing apparatus) in the event of an enclosed space emergency.

Figure 11.13
Checklists can be a useful aid for emergency situations

Step 5.3 – Contingency Equipment

All rescue and resuscitation equipment necessary to perform a rescue should be made available at the access point before any entry is made. All equipment should be checked and should be in a good operational condition.

Equipment should include breathing apparatus together with fully charged spare cylinders, lifelines and rescue harnesses, a recovery stretcher and torches approved for use in a flammable atmosphere. A means of hoisting an incapacitated person from the enclosed space may be required, depending on the nature of the space.

Code of Safe Working Practices for Merchant Seamen (COSWP)

Chapter 17
Entering Enclosed or Confined Spaces

http://shippingregs.org/14.re

Emergency escape breathing devices should not be worn as rescue equipment.

Figure 11.14
Emergency escape breathing devices should not be used for entry into enclosed spaces, these are provided for emergency escape

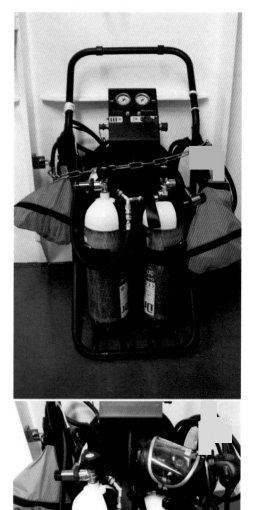

Figure 11.15
Rescue equipment should be available at the point of access

Case Study: *'Viking Islay'*

The *'Viking Islay'* was originally designed and built as an anchor handling and supply vessel in Spain in 1985. In 1991 it was converted to a Category B emergency response and rescue vessel (ERRV), suitable for the recovery and care of up to 300 survivors. The vessel was engaged in this role at the time of the incident, which was in 2007.

The vessel was supporting the self-elevating jack-up drilling rig *'Ensco 92'* in the Amethyst Gas Field, in the Southern North Sea, with a standard crew of 12. The crew consisted of British and Polish nationals with the common language spoken onboard being English. The majority of the crew were regular to the vessel and were experienced in ERRV operations.

Incident Summary

On Friday 21st September 2007, the *'Viking Islay'* berthed in Immingham for a routine port call that included bunkering operations, minor repairs and maintenance, stores and a full crew change. Prior to this port call, the starboard anchor had been cleared and readied for use in case of an emergency during port entry operations. The next day, the vessel sailed and the starboard anchor was stowed and secured for sea. The vessel arrived on location later that day and commenced its projected 28 day tour on station at the *'Ensco 92'*.

During the night and into the next morning of Sunday 23rd September, the motion of the ship was such that the starboard anchor chain was heard to repeatedly make contact with what

was believed to be the spurling pipe. This disturbed the sleep of those in the immediate vicinity of the chain locker.

Later the next morning, one of the able seamen informed the Master that they would like to enter the chain locker to secure the chain against further motion. This request was accepted by the Master and it was agreed that the space could be entered later in the morning, following the scheduled helicopter arrival and departure at the *'Ensco 92'*.

At approximately 10:55 hrs, after the departure of the helicopter, two crew members went forward to the chain locker. At this time the Master was not on the bridge. The crew members had a portable VHF with them, but no other equipment. No risk assessment was completed, no PTW was raised, no mechanical ventilation was used and the atmosphere within the locker was not tested.

The first crew member is believed to have entered the chain locker with the second remaining at the access point. Soon after entry, the seaman collapsed and the second seaman raised the alarm and then entered the space to assist. He also collapsed.

The able seaman who had been on the bridge at the time, immediately left the wheelhouse and proceeded to the chain locker, raising the alarm as he went. Both the Chief Officer and the Second Officer heard his cries and accompanied him to the foc'sle. On arrival at the entrance to the chain locker, it was clear that the two men who had entered were in serious trouble and their bodies could be seen at the foot of the locker. Donning breathing apparatus, the able seaman who had alerted the Chief Officer and Second Officer attempted to enter the chain locker. However, due to the lack of space, he was unable to do so. He removed the breathing apparatus and donned a short duration emergency escape breathing device (EEBD). Unfortunately, at some point, the hood of the EEBD became dislodged and this third seaman also collapsed.

By this time, the Master was on the bridge and had raised the alarm onboard, mustering all personnel, and had also requested assistance from the 'Ensco 92' and HM Coastguard.

At this point, the Chief Officer instructed one of the remaining able seamen to enter the space, wearing breathing apparatus to try and assist the latest casualty. Being smaller in stature he successfully entered the chain locker without incident and located the prone body of the latest casualty. With the assistance of another able seaman and the third engineer, the body of the latest casualty was recovered to the vessel's deck.

A rescue team, including a medic, was transferred from the 'Ensco 92' to assist the crew of the 'Viking Islay'. Together they recovered the bodies of the two crew members from the chain locker.

All three victims were transferred by helicopter ashore, but all died due to the oxygen deficient atmosphere in the chain locker.

Incident Investigation

The Marine Accident Investigation Branch (MAIB) conducted an extensive incident investigation that concluded that all three men died as a result of a lack of oxygen in the chain locker. The report highlighted a number of findings that are believed to have contributed to the loss of life.

The full findings are not reproduced here, however, the main findings have been collated and grouped into specific areas of operations.

 Marine Accident Investigation Branch (MAIB)

Report No. 12/2008

http://shippingregs.org/38.re

While the individual failures highlighted in the MAIB report are summarised here, it is evident that they were not isolated. All of them contributed to a more widespread system failure of the SMS, in the knowledge, awareness and training of the crew and in the inadequate and improper use of equipment.

- The SMS did not identify the enclosed spaces onboard the vessel and did not provide sufficient guidance regarding entry into enclosed spaces

- the SMS required a PTW to be in place prior to entry into an enclosed space. This was not complied with onboard the vessel and neither the Master nor the shore-based personnel had identified the ongoing failures in the system, although internal audits had been conducted

- inconsistencies had developed between the perceived intentions of the SMS, as expected by the shore-based management, and the working practices that had developed onboard the vessel

- the company had failed to identify the failures in the entry into enclosed space procedures practised onboard the vessel. The audit regime in place was inadequate

- the company management stated that it was their intention that entry into enclosed spaces should only be performed in port and with the assistance of shore-based expertise. This was not formally written in the company SMS

- a task risk assessment for entry into enclosed spaces was provided by the company. However, the task risk assessment did not identify the requirement to test the atmosphere prior to entry

- the SMS included the use of toolbox talks to identify hazards and control measures. No toolbox talk was recorded prior to the entry into the chain locker

- regular training sessions and drills may have provided the emergency teams with a better understanding of their roles in emergency situations

- training records indicated that familiarisation training in the use of EEBDs had been provided. However, more regular training sessions would have ensured that the crew were aware that EEBDs should not be used for the purpose of entering enclosed spaces

- routine training sessions and drills should have been utilised to familiarise personnel with rescue equipment and rescue operations in enclosed spaces, such as the chain lockers. If these had been conducted properly, the problems encountered during the rescue attempt may have been avoided

- there was a lack of suitable equipment onboard for testing the atmosphere within the tank

- the vessel was not provided with any portable fans or portable lighting. Portable fans would have allowed forced mechanical ventilation of the compartment prior to entry.

**IMO MSC/Circ.849 –
Guidelines for
the Performance,
Location, Use and
Care of Emergency
Escape Breathing
Devices**

EEBDs are not to
be used for fighting
fires, entering oxygen
deficient voids or tanks,
or worn by fire-fighters.
In these events, a self-
contained breathing
apparatus, which is
specifically suited for
such situations, should
be used.

Case Study: 'Sava Lake'

The gearless general cargo ship 'Sava
Lake' was built in 1990. The vessel was
constructed with a single cargo hold
which could be subdivided if required.

The vessel operated on the spot charter
market and had no regular trading
area. However, the vessel mainly
operated within Europe and North Africa
and carried a wide variety of general
cargoes. The vessel operated with a
crew of seven.

Incident Summary

As the 'Sava Lake' operated on a non-
liner service, the Master was advised
of the intended cargo prior to the
commencement of each new charter.
On this occasion, the Master was
provided with insufficient and conflicting
information and was uncertain about
the properties of the cargo.

The cargo was steel turnings, which
have a tendency to self-heat and
reduce the levels of oxygen in cargo
spaces. The 'Sava Lake' did have a
Document of Compliance (Special
Requirement for Ships Carrying
Dangerous Goods). However, the
certificate prohibited the carriage of
this type of cargo. The vessel had
been used for carrying this exact cargo
previously and there was a common
perception that the vessel was certified
for this.

Although unconvinced of the accuracy
of the cargo information supplied, the
Master did not check the Document
of Compliance and agreed to load the
cargo. There were also failures on
the part of shore management, those
responsible for loading the cargo and
the charterer of the vessel.

However, it should be noted that
had the vessel been carrying similar
cargoes with similar properties for
which it was correctly certified the
accident may well have still occurred,
although the crew awareness of the
potential hazards may have been
increased.

The Bill of Lading issued to the vessel
on completion of loading did not
contain any reference to the hazardous
nature of the cargo or any particular
instructions on correct loading
methods. It was raining during loading
and one particular recommendation
should have been to ensure that the
cargo remained dry. Once wet, the
steel turnings had a tendency to self-
heat.

Two separate cargoes of steel turnings
were loaded onboard the vessel in

Copenhagen and Horsens, Denmark in early January 2008. During both port calls, the cargo was wet and it was noted that it was raining during loading operations.

On arrival in Horsens, the cargo was emitting a noticeable odour. The Master, understandably, requested clarification from the cargo agent and the shore terminal. The Master was again advised that the cargo was not dangerous.

On completion of loading this second parcel of cargo, the vessel departed for Leixoes, Portugal. No declaration was made to the Master that the cargo was liable to self-heating.

During the transit of the Dover Strait, with adverse weather forecast, the vents on the forward deck, including those to the forward store, were secured. Two able seamen performed these duties and checked again the following morning on the integrity of the vessel. Due to the heavy weather, both men were given the following afternoon off.

Later that evening it was discovered that the two men were missing and the alarm was raised.

On completion of a thorough search of the vessel, the bodies of both men were found at the bottom of an access ladder inside the forward store. It was unclear why both men were in the forward store, but they had been overcome by the strong cargo vapours present in the space and the vessel diverted immediately to the nearest port where the bodies were recovered.

Incident Investigation

The investigation into the deaths of the two able seamen concentrated on the properties of the cargo being carried. It was clear from an early stage of the investigation that the factors leading to the deaths of the two men could be traced back to before the cargo was loaded onboard.

- The loading port managers did not identify the cargoes as dangerous and did not follow prescribed procedures to maintain the cargo in a safe condition. In reality the cargo was wet and was loaded untrimmed. These are the optimum conditions for self-heating of the cargo

- the Master was not provided with adequate information on the properties of the cargo. Had the cargo been identified correctly, the Master and crew may have been aware of the self-heating and oxygen depleting properties of the steel turnings

- although the Master did question the cargo information provided, he accepted the information and did not enquire further into the hazardous nature of the cargoes. He did not check the Document of Compliance (Special Requirement for Ships Carrying Dangerous Goods)

- the forward store had not been identified as an enclosed space. Due to the hazardous nature of the cargo, the forward store, being adjacent to the cargo hold, effectively became an enclosed space and not a working space

- as the forward store had not been identified as an enclosed space, the company procedures and PTW system had not been used for operations requiring entry

- the ventilation system for the cargo hold and forward store had been modified by a previous crew. These modifications had created a direct route for vapours from the cargo hold into the forward store

- the crew onboard at the time of the accident were not fully aware of the modifications that had been made to the ventilation system. Planned maintenance was in place, but it did not include a visual inspection of the entire system. This would have highlighted the modifications

- familiarisation onboard the vessel did not include awareness of enclosed spaces or the peculiarities of the cargo hold and forward store ventilation system.

Marine Accident Investigation Branch (MAIB)

Report No. 15/2008

http://shippingregs.org/39.re

12 Safe Use of Work Equipment

Equipment and systems fitted onboard can range from simple hand tools to complex machinery with multiple components. Although many items will be common to most ship types, such as mooring and anchor windlasses, cargo-related equipment can be considerably different. The design, construction, use and maintenance of particular equipment and systems can, therefore, vary markedly from one ship to another.

Figure 12.1
Some types of equipment are common to most ships

12.1 Regulations and Guidance

To ensure that systems and equipment are safe, certain duties are placed on shipping companies and these are detailed in the Merchant Shipping and Fishing Vessels (Provision and Use of Work Equipment) Regulations (PUWER). The regulations apply to all UK registered vessels and all vessels operating within UK waters.

Maritime & Coastguard Agency (MCA)

The Merchant Shipping and Fishing Vessels (Provision and Use of Work Equipment) Regulations 2006

http://shippingregs.org/40.re

The regulations are derived from the European Community (EC) Directive for the Safe Use of Work Equipment (1995). The basic guidance provided within this section can be applied to the regulatory requirements of many countries, as the aim of the regulations is generally the same; the selection, provision and use of safe work equipment.

12.2 Measures and Controls

The regulations require work equipment, whether permanently installed or temporary, to be suitable and sufficient for the task for which it is intended. To comply with this basic requirement, measures and controls must be in place throughout the lifetime of the equipment. Consideration must, therefore, be given to the suitability and safe use of the equipment during the design and planning stages, to procurement and installation and during use and maintenance onboard the vessel. This includes:

- Design of work equipment

- procurement

- suitability

- installation

- marking

- access and egress

- instructions and information

- operating procedures

- maintenance

- inspection

- training and competence

- assessments.

Design of Work Equipment

All equipment should be designed in accordance with specific and applicable marine industry standards and in compliance with any international or national standards. This includes any Flag State Administration requirements and any national standards for the intended area of operation of the vessel.

Equipment that is purpose-built should be designed with consideration of its

intended use and the environment in which it will be installed and operated. The safety of the user and maintenance personnel should also be considered at the design stage.

Procurement

Personnel tasked with the procurement of work equipment will often have no direct involvement with its use or maintenance. To avoid procurement of equipment not suited for the intended purpose, it is important that procurement personnel are guided by the users and maintenance personnel.

Suitability

Positioning of equipment will be a major consideration, as well as the interaction between the work equipment and any other previously installed permanent or temporary systems.

All equipment should be fitted with adequate protection for the user and maintenance personnel and have suitable safety features (emergency stops, cut-outs and safety guards).

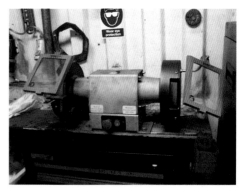

Figure 12.3
Work equipment should be designed to protect the user

Figure 12.2
Rotating machinery and machinery that could cause a hazard should be guarded

Installation

Work equipment should be secured to avoid any potential for movement, overturning or collapsing. Equipment should be stable in all anticipated conditions liable to be experienced. Adequate lighting (including emergency) and access arrangements should be put in place.

Marking

All work equipment should be marked to ensure that all controls are clear and unambiguous. This includes highlighting all emergency stop and safety functions.

Any limitations in the use of the equipment, such as safe working loads (SWLs), should be clearly marked.

Figure 12.4
Work equipment should be marked with relevant safe working limits

Any specific hazards should be marked. For example, if a guard should not be removed without the equipment first being electrically isolated, the danger of electrocution should be highlighted. Warning signs or alarms should be in place.

Access and Egress

Access to work equipment should be such that all users and maintenance personnel are not exposed to uncontrolled hazards. Similarly, personnel transiting or working in the vicinity of the equipment should not be exposed to any hazards in their routine tasks. Areas of potential hazard should, therefore, be segregated and access restricted.

In the event of failure of the equipment or any other foreseeable emergency, an escape route to safety must also be available. Consideration must be given to all potential failures and how they would impact the user or maintenance crew in their working positions.

Figure 12.5
Access for maintenance should be considered

Instructions and Information

The equipment manufacturer should provide instructions and guidance on the safe use and maintenance of the equipment, including details of the safety functions, any specific hazards and all limitations. Minimum levels of routine maintenance should be stated and instructions should be provided detailing the methodology to be followed to conduct maintenance operations safely.

Any emergency instructions, such as emergency lowering procedures for a crane, should be clearly stated and, ideally, in pictorial form.

Figure 12.6
Crane operators must be familiar with all safety and operational functions

Operating Procedures

Although the manufacturer will be expected to provide instructions and information on the equipment, company or vessel-specific operating procedures should also be put in place. For example, while opening a hatch on a cargo ship is a simple operation if the manufacturer's methodology is followed, on a specific vessel it may be necessary to ensure a particular

crane is in the stowed position to avoid contact.

Maintenance

The ISM Code requires all companies to establish procedures to ensure the ship is maintained in accordance with all relevant rules and regulations.

Maintenance may include the use of a PTW system and documented isolation procedures.

The need for additional training for maintenance personnel on specific equipment should always be considered.

Figure 12.7
Access to machinery for maintenance purposes should be restricted to appropriate personnel

Inspection

Equipment should be regularly inspected to ensure that any defects are highlighted and rectified in a timely manner. Regular inspection will also determine if any changes to the environment or operating practices have occurred. The equipment should remain fit for purpose.

Inspections should be conducted, as a minimum, in line with the manufacturer's instructions and guidance. Consideration should always be given to the environment and the expected use the equipment will be exposed to.

Figure 12.8
The condition of all component parts should be inspected

Training and Competence

Companies should implement and maintain an effective training system to ensure the competency of all persons involved in the use and maintenance of work equipment. This can include attendance at equipment

manufacturers' courses, onboard training and assessment by third party experts.

Figure 12.9
Training may be required for users and maintenance personnel for specific work equipment, such as deck cranes

Assessments

Assessments should consider all aspects of the safe use and maintenance of work equipment from the design and procurement stage, to operating procedures, training, competence and routine maintenance.

The assessment process should eliminate, mitigate or control risks arising from the equipment installation, design or operation, that might reasonably be foreseen. Assessments should be reviewed on a regular basis and on any change of the working environment, position of the equipment, use of the equipment or other circumstance that may affect the safety of personnel.

Figure 12.10
Assessments can be conducted on any type of equipment – including cranes

13 Mooring

Mooring and unmooring operations, irrespective of the ship type and design, should always be considered high risk activities. Mooring and unmooring operations take place either on arrival in port, when seafarers may have experienced fatigue due to poor weather conditions, or on departure from port after protracted and intense cargo loading and discharging operations.

Even experienced seafarers have been the victims of mooring-related accidents and every year many seafarers are seriously or fatally injured.

Figure 13.1
Mooring and unmooring operations take place at stressful times

Failures to permanent equipment, parting of wires/ropes and wires/ropes jumping and slipping off drum ends and mooring bitts are the most likely causes of injury.

23%	Leg
14%	Fatal
14%	Back
11%	Multiple
7%	Head
7%	Arm
24%	Others

Table 13.1
Mooring Incident Injuries (UK P&I Club)

13.1 Assessing the Risk

It is essential that all marine crew consider the safety aspects of mooring and unmooring onboard their vessels, with particular reference to:

- The design, construction, layout and maintenance of the permanent mooring equipment

- the selection of temporary mooring equipment including ropes, wires and stoppers

- snap-back zones and hazards associated with the permanent and temporary mooring equipment

- safe mooring practices, taking into consideration the equipment available and the layout of the mooring station.

13.2 Permanent Mooring Equipment

- Mooring winches, windlasses, mooring bitts and all associated equipment should be designed and constructed with due regard to the dimensions, tonnage, range of drafts and loading conditions of the vessel and, therefore, the expected loads and stresses

- all permanent mooring equipment should be designed and constructed with due consideration to the ports and berths where the vessel is likely to regularly visit. This is of particular importance for RoRo vessels and other ship types on regular feeder runs between specific ports

Figure 13.2
Permanent mooring equipment should be positioned to provide adequate mooring configurations

- all permanent equipment should be positioned to provide the most efficient and safe mooring operations and to provide a number of options for mooring at different ports and berths. The use of roller

fairleads to ensure ropes and wires are led clear of all obstruction, nips and edges is essential

- permanent equipment should be positioned so that maximum protection is afforded to the crew

- mooring station decks should be treated with anti-slip surfaces and any walkways or control positions should be fitted with anti-slip surfaces and handholds

- lighting in mooring stations should ensure all surfaces and areas are well illuminated during periods of darkness

- all controls for permanent mooring winches and windlasses must be suitably marked and any emergency stops must be clearly identified

- instructions for permanent mooring equipment must be available and particular attention should be paid to ensuring that instructions for the use of specific functions, such as tensioning devices, are provided

- all permanent mooring equipment should be assessed in accordance with the Safe Use of Work Equipment Regulations. Assessments should consider the maintenance and safe use of the mooring equipment for all expected circumstances

- regular planned maintenance schedules to conduct routine maintenance and checks on all permanent mooring equipment should be in place in line with the manufacturer's instructions. Routine checks should also be used to identify any damage, defects or signs of stress that may affect the operational capability or safety of any personnel using the equipment. Any alarm systems or cut outs fitted should be checked during routine maintenance schedules.

13.3   Temporary Mooring Equipment

Temporary mooring equipment includes the mooring ropes, mooring wires and ancillary equipment such as heaving lines and stoppers. Although this equipment will be replaced on a regular basis, the same care and attention must be given to the process for selecting, using and maintaining it as for permanent equipment.

- It should be selected to be compatible with the permanent mooring equipment. Mooring ropes, for example, should be of a size (diameter) suitable for the winch drum, which may be grooved

- mooring rope and wire breaking loads should be appropriate for the winch and drum end capabilities. Mooring ropes with a higher strength rating than the mooring system can result in failure of the winches, with potentially fatal results

- mooring winches, windlasses, mooring bitts and all associated equipment must be designed and constructed with due regard to the dimensions, tonnage, range of

draughts and loading conditions of the vessel and therefore the expected loads and stresses

- mooring ropes and wires should be selected with due regard to the dimensions, tonnage, range of draughts and loading conditions of the vessel. This should include consideration for providing mooring ropes and wires of sufficient length and breaking loads for the anticipated mooring configurations at regular berths and ports

Figure 13.3
Mooring ropes should be protected at high contact areas to avoid excessive wear

- mooring ropes, where possible, should be stowed clear of the deck, out of direct sunlight and clear of any possible sources of contamination. Where mooring ropes are permanently stowed on winch drums, suitable covers should be put in place to provide protection

- mooring ropes should be provided with protection at areas of high contact (eyes) to avoid excessive wear

- where mooring ropes are stowed on storage reels, they should not be deployed directly during mooring operations. They should be run off and flaked on the deck prior to being deployed in a safe and controlled manner

- mooring ropes and wires should be visually inspected prior to and after use and at regular periods. Any defects should be rectified and mooring ropes and wires replaced as necessary. Wire ropes should be maintained in accordance with the manufacturer's recommendations.

Figure 13.5
Ropes and wires that part whilst under tension will recoil, with considerable force, in the direction of the tension and therefore one of the most important considerations for mooring operations is the identification of any 'snap-back' zones

Figure 13.4
Mooring ropes should be routinely inspected

13.4 Snap-Back Zones and Hazard Identification

Most mooring-related injuries are caused by mooring ropes or wires failing while under strain.

The identification of 'snap-back' zones and other mooring-related hazards should be identified as part of the risk assessment process.

- Access points to the mooring stations should be reviewed. Signage should be put in place to prevent personnel accessing the mooring stations

- mooring stations should be reviewed for trip hazards. These can be considerable at mooring stations where either pipework for permanently installed machinery or raised surfaces may be a potential hazard. Any trip hazards should be removed if possible, highlighted or covered (pipe covers, ramps)

- slip hazards can be a potential hazard where grease and oil can accumulate from fixed mooring equipment. Any slip hazards should be treated or removed immediately and the sources of the hazard investigated and rectified

- mooring stations can often have raised platforms for winch controls and consideration must be given to ensuring that all operators have safe access to these areas and that adequate protection (handrails) is provided

- mooring rope stowage positions, access to and from these positions and the methods used for retrieving and stowing the ropes should be reviewed. Safe access and a suitable means for ensuring the task can be completed in a safe manner must be provided. Stowage positions should not block any emergency or access arrangements

- an overview diagram of 'snap-back' zones should be put in place and made available to all personnel

DON'T RISK LIFE AND LIMB!
KEEP CLEAR OF SNAP BACK ZONES

FACT: A crew member was struck by a mooring rope and **died from multiple injuries.**

Maritime and Coastguard Agency, Spring Place, 105 Commercial Road, Southampton SO15 1EG. Telephone: 023 8032 9227

© Crown Copyright. Paper 75% PCW and 25% ECF pulp. Ref: MCA/137

Figure 13.6
All crew must be aware of 'snap-back' zones

- there should be adequate lighting at all control points and in way of all mooring equipment and leads. Emergency lighting should also be provided

- if the berthing arrangements for the vessel are such that the same mooring line configuration is deployed on a regular basis, it may be prudent to identify the 'snap-back' zones by highlighting the hazardous areas on the deck. This may help to ensure that the crew keep clear of these areas.

13.5 Safe Mooring Practices

Safe mooring practices will, to a certain extent, depend on the mooring equipment onboard and the mooring configuration at the berth or port. However, general guidance on safe mooring practices is available from a number of respected sources including the COSWP and Mooring Equipment Guidelines (OCIMF).

- Mooring stations should be restricted areas and only personnel directly involved and essential to the mooring operations should be permitted within the immediate vicinity. This restricted access should continue during port call periods as changing tide levels, changing vessel loading conditions and other vessel movements can cause considerable strain on mooring equipment and pose a potential hazard

Figure 13.7
Mooring stations should be designated as restricted areas

Figure 13.8
Good communications with shore-based linemen is essential

- the number of personnel required to form a mooring party will depend on the equipment available, the berthing arrangements and the mooring configuration. Mooring operations should not take place without an appropriate number of experienced personnel suitable for the circumstances

- the deck officer in charge of mooring operations should be in direct and constant communication with the bridge and should oversee all communications with the shore linemen. Where portable radios are used, the vessel name should be clearly identified in any communications to avoid misinterpretation

- the deck officer in charge of the mooring operation should not be involved in any physical tasks, but should monitor all operations to ensure that any hazards are identified in suitable time and to ensure that all operations are conducted and controlled in a safe manner. The deck officer should be positioned to have direct line of sight with the winch operators and the shore-based linemen

- in instances where less experienced members of the marine crew are assigned to mooring stations, they should be under the supervision and direction of an experienced member of the mooring party

- the deck officer and all assigned crew should be made aware of the proposed mooring configuration at the berth or port. Any changes to the proposed plan should be suitably assessed

- the deck officer and all crew assigned to the mooring station should be aware of the safe use of the mooring equipment and the capabilities and limitations of all winches, windlasses and ancillary equipment, including ropes and wires

- the proposed mooring configuration should be arranged to ensure the maximum effectiveness of the moorings. Back springs and breast lines provide the most effective mooring restraint respectively. Overly long mooring leads and short leads should be avoided and consideration should be given to ensuring that mooring lines are not obstructed or do not make contact with any installations on the berth

- personnel assigned to the mooring party should be familiar with and experienced in the use of the mooring winches. Competent personnel should only be used for operating all mooring equipment

- all crew should be provided with and should utilise all appropriate PPE including hard hats, safety boots, coveralls and, where appropriate, eye protection when winch handling. Gloves may be worn to provide protection, but consideration must be given to the fact that ill-fitting gloves can be a serious hazard

- all members of the mooring party must be aware of the hazards associated with mooring operations including 'snap-back' zones. All crew should be aware of the particular 'snap-back' zones for that vessel and mooring configuration

- awareness of bights and the associated hazards must always be considered during all mooring operations.

Mooring Safety
Personnel should NEVER stand in a bight of wire or rope

- mooring equipment should be prepared in time to ensure that mooring operations can be conducted in a controlled and safe manner. Mooring ropes should be flaked out ready for deployment to avoid bights

- mooring ropes and wires should not be deployed through the same fairlead or secured on the same mooring bitts. Such practices are likely to lead to damage to the ropes or wires

- winch and windlass operators should have a clear and unobstructed view of the mooring area

Figure 13.11
Mooring ropes should, where possible, be led through different rollers or leads

Figure 13.9
Personnel operating winches should always remain at the control station and should not use any control extensions

- personnel tending mooring lines on the drum ends during mooring operations should only tend the specific mooring line and should not conduct other operations at the same time

- mooring lines recovered should be flaked in a controlled manner clear of the immediate drum end area. A second person, where available, should assist with flaking the mooring line

- mooring ropes should not be secured on drum ends. Drum ends are not designed to withstand such loads and mooring ropes should be turned up on mooring bitts

- when taking the tension on mooring ropes on the drum end, a maximum of three turns should be sufficient to prevent surging. More contact than necessary between the drum end and the mooring ropes will result in damage to the ropes

Figure 13.10
Rope and wire bights pose a potential hazard during mooring operations

- mooring ropes and wires should, where necessary, be stoppered off as per the instructions and guidance provided by the manufacturer and COSWP.

Maritime and
Coastguard Agency

Code of Safe Working
Practices for Merchant
Seamen (COSWP)

http://shippingregs.org/14.re

Figure 13.12
*Drum ends are not designed to withstand
loads for prolonged periods*

Case Study: *'Dublin Viking'*

The *'Dublin Viking'* is a RoRo passenger ferry built in 1997. The 21,856 gross tonnage vessel is 178 metres long and has a beam of 25 metres. The ferry has a total capacity for 340 passengers in a mixture of cabins and reclining seats. A total of 140 trailers can be loaded in the vessel's RoRo decks.

At the time of the accident, the vessel was on a regular trading pattern between Birkenhead, Liverpool and Dublin. This trading pattern was quite intensive and during any seven-day period the vessel conducted approximately 24 berthing and un-berthing operations. Mooring operations were, therefore, routine onboard the vessel and standard mooring configurations were used.

Report on the
investigation of the
parting of a mooring line
on board *'Dublin Viking'*
resulting in one fatality

MAIB Report No.
7/2008

http://shippingregs.org/42.re

Incident Summary

In the late evening of 7th August 2007, loading of the *'Dublin Viking'* had been completed and the vessel was preparing to depart from Dublin, bound for Liverpool.

The after mooring party consisted of the Second Officer, four able seamen and one ordinary seaman. Immediately on completion of loading operations, the mooring party assembled, with the Second Officer the last to arrive as he was assisting the Chief Officer with loading operations.

The ordinary seaman was at the winch controls for the after ramp and the stern line that was the subject of the resulting accident. The Second Officer was positioned on the starboard quarter where he could pass instructions to both the shore mooring party and the mooring party on deck.

At 22:14 hrs, the Master instructed the Second Officer to let go the stern line. At this time, the after ramp was in the process of being raised by the ordinary seaman using the controls close by the stern line mooring winch.

The ordinary seaman was instructed to slacken the tension on the stern line to allow the shore mooring party to release the line from the mooring bollard. As he operated both the after ramp controls and the stern line controls, the tension on the stern line was noted to increase.

Figure 13.13
Drum ends are not designed for
excessive loads

During the previous berthing operation, the stern line had been turned up on the drum end with approximately five turns to secure the vessel alongside.

Due to the tension on the line, the able seamen felt that they should keep clear of the drum end as they could not clear the turns from the drum. The ordinary seaman therefore attempted to slacken the tension again using the winch controls, while still raising the after ramp with the ramp controls. The

mooring winch (and drum end) turned in the opposite direction to what was intended and the tension in the stern line was such that it parted.

The parted line struck the Second Officer who dropped immediately to the deck with severe injuries to both legs. Both legs were broken and one had been almost severed. Immediate medical attention was administered by the marine crew until the injured officer could be tended by paramedics. The Second Officer was transported to hospital where his left leg was subsequently amputated. He died as a result of his injuries, six days after the accident.

Incident Investigation

The subsequent investigation into the accident found:

- There had been no formal assessment of the mooring stations, mooring configurations, mooring equipment or safe practices. Such an assessment should have been conducted to consider the suitability of the equipment, the practicality of the mooring arrangement and to identify 'snap-back' zones. The lack of identification of 'snap-back' zones had been raised during an inspection by the company marine and safety manager, but had not been rectified

- the lead of the stern line was such that it changed direction a number of times on the deck of the vessel, with a resulting increase in the number of 'snap-back' zones and potential hazards

- the Second Officer had to stand in a number of 'snap-back' zones during mooring operations. Although the after mooring station area was considered quite cramped, a proper assessment of the mooring station could have highlighted these potentially hazardous areas

- the condition of the stern line was found to have deteriorated significantly since it was purchased. This could be attributed to a number of factors, including excessive wear and tear (lead of wires and frequent use) and the fact that the mooring ropes were stored on deck in direct sunlight and unprotected from contact with any potential contaminants

- there was no evidence available to confirm whether the mooring ropes had been routinely and regularly inspected. Provisions for inspecting the mooring ropes were not included in the ship's planned maintenance system and no certification could be found for any of the mooring ropes onboard

- procedures were in place requiring the Deck Officers to inspect the mooring ropes prior to mooring operations. However, this was impracticable as the officers were always involved in loading operations until immediately before mooring operations commenced

- the ordinary seaman was involved in two simultaneous operations, using controls that were in very close proximity and which operated in opposite directions. When attempting to slacken the mooring rope he had, in effect, increased the tension. The ordinary seaman was, however, aware of the status of the winch control markings and the operation of the winch

- if a safe use of work equipment assessment had been conducted on the mooring winch, it may have highlighted the inadequacy of the marking of the controls

- the marine crew were aware of the problem with the winch controls, but had accepted the issue. The problem had not been raised during any safety inspections or audits prior to the accident and complacency and acceptance of defects was highlighted

- the winch controls were not marked clearly and provided no indication that the winch operated in the opposite manner to all the other winches on the after deck. A further potential hazard was that the controls did not return to a neutral position when let go by the operator

- the practice of using winch drum ends for securing mooring ropes is not recommended. Drum ends are not designed to withstand anticipated loads expected during periods alongside and mooring ropes should be secured to mooring bitts. Complacency and acceptance of unsafe mooring practices were highlighted

- the mooring winches and bitts were not the original installations and the mooring equipment had changed gradually over the years. Insufficient information was available to allow the crew to select appropriate mooring ropes for use with the winches or to determine the capabilities or limits of the equipment

- some roller fairleads on the after deck were noted to be seized and some scaling, wear and corrosion was evident. Evidence was available to suggest that rust scaling had snagged the mooring line. Although it is not certain that this contributed directly to the accident, it can be assumed that such conditions can cause deterioration to mooring ropes over a period of time

- the stern mooring was made up of component parts from the ship and from the shore. The component parts had evolved with no consideration of the whole mooring line system

- a risk assessment was in place for mooring operations. However, several of the control measures could not be implemented in practice

- in addition to the lack of a formalised and documented inspection regime for the mooring ropes, there was no adequate process in place for training the crew in such skills or for identifying and replacing old mooring ropes with suitable new ropes of the correct specification, particularly minimum breaking loads. No replacement criteria was in place.

Figure 13.14
Maintenance of mooring equipment
is essential

14 Accident Investigations

Introduction

Accident investigations are often considered external tasks to be conducted onboard a ship by a third party expert.

For serious accidents, this will be the case due to the obligations imposed on the Flag State Authorities by the IMO. However, due to the nature of the shipping industry the site of the accident might be days away from the nearest port and vital evidence may be lost if no action is taken onboard. Shipboard personnel, and in particular the Safety Officer and Master, must therefore, in such circumstances, do all within their powers to assist the investigators.

In addition, for minor accidents, it is standard practice for the marine crew to conduct an internal investigation to identify the underlying causes of the incident and any recommendations that may prevent a similar occurrence on the ship, sister ships, company ships or any other vessel.

As a result of any accident or dangerous occurrence, the designated Safety Officer has a duty to investigate and should do so at the soonest opportunity. This will be irrespective of whether a third party incident investigation will be conducted as the Safety Officer will be able to obtain witness accounts of the accident and inspect the accident site in a timely manner. If the ship is several days or even hours from port, witness testimony can become tainted and the accident site can be altered intentionally or inadvertently (by the weather for example).

14.1 Regulations and Guidance

The IMO sets minimum requirements and standards and provides guidance to Flag State Administrations in relation to marine accidents (casualty investigations). The obligation imposed on the Flag State Administrations is detailed in Regulation 6 of Chapter XI-1 of SOLAS.

Figure 14.1
Accident investigations can help promote lessons learned

SOLAS - Chapter XI-1
Special Measures to Enhance Maritime Safety

Each Administration shall conduct investigations of marine casualties and incidents, in accordance with the provisions of the present Convention, as supplemented by the provisions of the Code of the International Standards and Recommended Practices for a Safety Investigation into a Marine Casualty or Marine Incident (Casualty Investigation Code)

To ensure that the obligation to conduct an investigation is completed in a methodical manner, using a common approach, the IMO has issued detailed guidance in the form of the Casualty Investigation Code.

Casualty Investigation Code

The objective of this code is to provide a common approach for states to adopt in the conduct of marine safety investigations into marine casualties and marine incidents

---

The Casualty Investigation Code promotes the use of all types of evidence, including physical evidence, witness statements and documentary evidence, to identify the immediate causal factors and any underlying conditions associated with the accident.

Investigators are provided with the authority to thoroughly investigate all circumstances surrounding an accident and are authorised to board the ship, interview all relevant personnel onboard and to obtain any evidence required to conduct the investigation. The investigation must be independent, to ensure an impartial approach, and should be used as an invaluable tool to prevent marine casualties and marine incidents onboard the subject vessel, the company fleet, vessels of the Flag State and within the shipping industry.

The resulting marine safety investigation report and associated recommendations should be made available to the IMO so that the lessons learned can be distributed to all interested parties within the shipping industry. The purpose of a marine accident investigation should always be to ensure that an identical or similar accident does not occur on the same or any other vessel. The transparency of the investigation findings is, therefore, essential.

IMO Definition of 'Very Serious Marine Casualty'

A marine casualty involving the total loss of the ship or a death or severe damage to the environment.

An event, or a sequence of events, that has resulted in any of the following which has occurred directly in connection with the operations of a ship	
Persons involved	The death of, or serious injury to, a person
	The loss of a person from a ship
Ship involved	The loss, presumed loss or abandonment of a ship
	Material damage to a ship
	The stranding or disabling of a ship
	The involvement of a ship in a collision
Equipment and systems involved	Material damage to marine infrastructure external to a ship, that could seriously endanger the safety of the ship, another ship or an individual
	Severe damage to the environment, or the potential for severe damage to the environment, brought about by the damage of a ship or ships

Table 14.1
IMO definition of 'Marine Casualty'

IMO definition of a 'Marine Incident'

An event, or sequence of events, other than a marine casualty, which has occurred directly in connection with the operations of a ship that endangered, or, if not corrected, would endanger the safety of the ship, its occupants or any other person or the environment

---

14.2 Marine Accident Investigation Branch (MAIB)

In the UK, the Maritime and Coastguard Agency (MCA) is the recognised Flag State Authority. However, for accidents involving UK flagged vessels or for accidents within UK territorial waters, the authority and responsibility for conducting investigations has been delegated to the Marine Accident Investigation Branch (MAIB). The MAIB is a separate division within the Department of Transport and is not part of the MCA. For vessels operating under the jurisdiction of other Flag State Authorities, different reporting and investigation requirements will apply. However, the information detailed here is provided as an example.

The Merchant Shipping (Accident Reporting and Investigation) Regulations define the role and responsibilities of the MAIB, specify the reporting requirements for applicable vessels, defines the circumstances under which an incident must be reported and investigated and also the standards to be applied during the conduct of an investigation.

The obligation to report an accident onboard or involving a United Kingdom registered vessel is the responsibility of the ship's Master and the owner.

Serious injuries must be reported and the findings of the owner's own investigation reported to the MAIB within 14 days of the accident. Once reported, the role of the MAIB becomes central to the investigation process.

It is the remit of the Chief Inspector of the MAIB to decide whether an investigation will be conducted by the MAIB and what form the investigation will take. In these circumstances, the Chief Inspector has far reaching powers to ensure that the vessel (site of the accident) is available for inspection and may take whatever action is necessary to maintain the available evidence. In addition, the Chief Inspector and his deputies will have full access to any documentary evidence and information, including voyage data recorders, to assist with the successful and thorough investigation of the accident.

However, the Chief Inspector may decide that an investigation conducted by the owner is sufficient.

The investigation by the MAIB will include a review of all available

Persons involved	*Any occurrence on board a ship or involving a ship whereby there is loss of life or major injury to any person on board, or any person is lost or falls overboard from, the ship or one of its ship's boats*
Ship involved	*The ship causes any loss of life, major injury or material damage*
	The ship is lost or is presumed to be lost
	The ship is abandoned
	The ship is materially damaged by fire, explosion, weather or other cause
	The ship grounds
	The ship is in a collision
	The ship is disabled and not under command for a period of more than 12 hours or requires assistance to reach port
	The ship causes significant harm to the environment
Equipment and systems involved	*A collapse or bursting of any pressure vessel, pipeline or valve*
	A collapse or failure of any lifting equipment, access equipment, hatch cover, staging, bosun's chair or any associated load bearing parts
	Collapse of cargo, unintended movement of cargo or ballast sufficient to cause a list, or loss of cargo overboard
	A snagging of fishing gear which results in the vessel heeling to a dangerous angle
	A contact by a person with loose asbestos fibre except when full protective clothing is worn
	An escape of any harmful substance or agent

Table 14.2
Definition of 'Accident' according to the UK MS Regulations

documentation (log books, charts), interviews with all those personnel directly involved with the accident, witnesses and an inspection of any specific areas onboard the vessel. Conclusions relating to the incident will be recorded in a formal investigation report, based on this evidence, judgement and analysis of the investigation team.

The report will be issued with all applicable recommendations raised as a result of the investigation. These recommendations will be addressed to the relevant parties, which may include the vessel owner, Master and Flag State Administration. On completion and issue of the final investigation report to the interested parties, the MAIB may consider, depending on the circumstances of the accident, issuing a safety alert or the full report to all sectors of the marine industry.

 The Merchant Shipping (Accident Reporting and Investigation) Regulations

http://shippingregs.org/43.re

14.3 Onboard Reporting of Accidents

The reporting of accidents onboard a UK registered vessel or a vessel operating within UK waters is the responsibility of the ship's Master and the owner. The Master (or senior surviving officer) or representative of the shipowner must report the accident to the MAIB as soon as practicable.

Information to be provided to the MAIB includes:

- The name of the ship

- IMO number or official number

- name and address of the shipowner

- name of the Master

- date and time of the incident

- geographical position of the incident

- passage details for the ship; last port and next port

- brief details of the accident and the sequence of events leading to the accident

- type and extent of the damage to the ship

- any loss of life or injuries suffered and the details of the relevant personnel

- any potential or actual pollution to the environment as a result of the incident

- any potential or actual hazard to navigation as a result of the incident

- name and port of registry of any other vessel(s) involved in the incident

- the make and model of the voyage data recorder fitted onboard

- weather conditions.

14.4 Onboard Investigation of Accidents

The obligation on the Master or the owners to report an accident to the MAIB, under the requirements of the Merchant Shipping (Accident Reporting and Investigation) Regulations, does not exonerate either party from investigating the accident and from providing an investigation report. Such an investigation should be conducted onboard and the report and any recommendations should be provided to the MAIB within 14 days of the accident.

ISM Code

"The safety management system should include procedures ensuring that non-conformities, accidents and hazardous situations are reported to the company, investigated and analysed with the objective of improving safety and pollution prevention"

14.5 Accident Area and Preservation of Evidence

- The accident site should be secured to preserve any evidence. This includes sealing off the area against further injury or damage

- the Safety Officer should inspect the area to identify any factors that may have contributed to the accident. Photographs of the site may provide significant assistance to future investigations. It may be advantageous for the Safety Officer to be accompanied by a crew member with expert knowledge of the area, such as the Chief Engineer in the engine room, as they may be able to provide an insight into the accident or highlight failures that may only be obvious to an expert

- the positions of any injured parties at the time of the accident and the location and extent of any damage to equipment or the ship's structure should be noted. Diagrams and sketches with distances marked will be of particular assistance

- all relevant environmental factors at the time of the accident should be noted, including the weather conditions and the effects they had on the accident

- any notable hazards that may have been a contributory factor in the incident should be noted and photographed

- documentary evidence should be preserved, including any applicable navigational charts, log books, work permits, risk assessments and any other written evidence that may be considered pertinent to the investigation

- any physical evidence, such as broken or damaged machine parts, should be quarantined and held for inspection by the investigators.

Code of Safe Working Practices for Merchant Seamen (COSWP)

"The Safety Officer has a duty to investigate notifiable accidents or dangerous occurrences affecting persons on board ship or during access"

14.6   Witness Statements

All persons, including any injured parties, witnesses and other persons connected with the accident, should be identified and statements should be obtained as soon as practically possible.

Any personnel not present at the time of the incident, but who were involved in earlier discussions concerning the operation that was being performed or who may have responsibility for the work or area of the operation should also be interviewed.

Interviews should be conducted in an informal atmosphere to relax the witness and put them at ease. Interviews should follow a structured approach.

The witness should be requested to relate the incident as accurately as possible from start to finish with little or no interruption. They should be requested to concentrate on the facts and avoid expressing opinions. Any inconsistencies between this version of the events and any others provided, and any details that may require to be clarified, should be noted and should be checked after the initial run through of events.

Once clarification and further questioning has been completed, the interviewer should repeat the details of the statement to the witness in order to check that they have been accurately recorded.

If satisfied with the accuracy of the statement, the witness should be asked to sign and date the document.

14.7   Voyage Data Recorders (VDRs)

While the use of data recorders has been commonplace in aviation incident investigations for many years a similar system for recording critical information relating to the voyage of a seagoing vessel has only relatively recently been implemented.

International Convention for the Safety of Life at Sea (SOLAS) – Chapter V – Safety of Navigation	
Cargo Ships	*All cargo ships of 3,000 gross tonnage and upwards and built on or after 1st July 2002, must be fitted with a Voyage Data Recorder.*
Passenger Ships	*All passenger ships built on or after 1st July 2002, must be fitted with a Voyage Data Recorder.*

VDRs are fitted externally in a protective storage unit that protects the VDR if in the event of a collision, fire, explosion or if the vessel were to sink. In the event of the loss of the vessel or following a serious incident, the information recorded by the unit in the proceeding 12 hours can be recovered and used to assist in the analysis of the incident.

Figure 14.2
Voyage Data Recorder

Following on from an accident, the Master and Safety Officer should ensure that all VDR information is maintained and ensure that the information is not overwritten. VDR information should be provided to the Flag State Authority investigators in the same way as all other documentary and physical evidence.

Information available from the VDR includes:

- Date and time

- position of the ship

- ship's speed and heading

- radar and/or automatic identification system (AIS) information

- bridge voice recordings

- VHF radio communication recordings

- echo sounder information

- status of hull openings, watertight doors and fire doors

- rudder, engine and manoeuvring systems status and movements

- weather data.

Appendix 1

Maritime and Coastguard Agency

The Merchant Shipping and Fishing Vessels Personal Protective Equipment Regulations 1999

This Merchant Shipping Notice is an integral part of the Merchant Shipping and Fishing Vessels (Personal Protective Equipment) Regulations 1999.

Notice to employers of crew, masters, safety officers and safety representatives.

This Notice supersedes Merchant Shipping Notices No. M1195 and M1358.

Summary

- This Notice gives notice of new regulations governing the provision of personal protective equipment, the Merchant Shipping and Fishing Vessels (Personal Protective Equipment) Regulations 1999. These Regulations supersede the Merchant Shipping (Protective Clothing and Equipment) Regulations 1985 (S.I. No. 1664), and come into force on 25 October 1999

- Annex 1 gives the design standards for personal protective equipment in use on board ships, for specified work activities and situations, in order to comply with regulation 5(2)(a) of the new Regulations.

Introduction

1. The Regulations require employers to ensure that personal protective equipment (PPE) is provided for their workers who are engaged in, or at risk from, a hazardous work activity on board a United Kingdom ship[1].

---

[1] "worker" includes trainees and apprentices, but does not include persons who are training in a sail training vessel.

2. The Regulations are subject to the general rule that use of PPE is always a last resort, where risks cannot be avoided or reduced to a safe level by means of collective protection, or safe systems of work.

3. PPE must be provided free of charge to the workers, except that, where use of the equipment is not exclusive to the work place, workers may be required to contribute towards the cost.

4. Where, traditionally, workers provide their own PPE, the employer remains responsible for ensuring that workers are equipped with appropriate PPE, and that they use it when engaged in work of the types outlined in <u>Annex 1</u>.

5. The equipment issued must be "suitable", which is defined as:

(a) in relation to any work process described in [this] Merchant Shipping Notice MSN 1731 (M+F), of the kind and to the standard specified [in that Merchant Shipping Notice], in relation to that work process;

(b) appropriate for the risks to which he worker is exposed and to the task which he is performing, without itself leading to any increased risk;

(c) correctly fitting the worker, or capable of being adjusted to fit;

(d) taking into account ergonomic requirements and the worker's state of health; and

(e) compatible with any other equipment the worker has to use at the same time, so that it continues to be effective against the risk"

6. In addition, the employer must ensure that the PPE supplied is easily accessible, and properly stored and maintained, and that where appropriate, instructions are available to the workers who are required to carry out any maintenance. The equipment must be regularly inspected, in accordance with the manufacturers instructions, and its operation checked. Respiratory protective equipment must be always be checked before and after use.

7. The employer must ensure, so far as is reasonably practicable, that PPE issued under the regulations is used as instructed - eg that workers do not use it for a purpose for which it is not designed, and that it is put on and worn correctly.

8. Workers must receive adequate and appropriate training so that they are aware of the risks against which the PPE is designed to protect them, and of when and how to use it and look after it correctly. This may include demonstrations of the wearing of PPE, where appropriate.

9. Workers are required to wear and use the PPE which has been issued to them when appropriate, and to comply with any training and instruction provided.

Standards of design and manufacture

10. The specifications for PPE are set out in the Annex. The list covers the PPE most commonly used on ships, but is not exclusive.

11. The letters "EN" stand for "European Norm". Where no "EN" standard is available, a BS standard is quoted. The letters "BS" refer to a British Standard. The standards are those to which the clothing and equipment should comply and the date which appears will be the date

on which the latest revision of the relevant Standard was published, including all amendments at the date of this Merchant Shipping Notice.

12. **Any reference to an EN or BS standard contained in the annex means that standard or an alternative Standard which provides, in use, equivalent levels of safety, suitability and fitness for purpose.**

13. The standards of equipment given in this Merchant Shipping Notice <u>do not apply</u> to life saving appliances or other equipment which is subject to the Merchant Shipping (Marine Equipment) Regulations. (S.I. 1999/1957).

14. Publications mentioned in Annex 1 are available from:

"BS" and "EN" Specifications:

The British Standards Institution
389 Chiswick High Road
London
W4 4AL

The Code of Practice, **"Noise Levels in Ships"** is available from The Stationery Office.

MSPP3 (Seafarers Health and Safety)
The Maritime and Coastguard Agency
Bay 2/1
Spring Place
105 Commercial Road
Southampton
SO15 1EG

Tel: 01703 329390
Fax: 01703 329251

August 1999

© Crown copyright 1999
[MC 122/6/053]

An executive agency of the Department of the Environment, Transport and the Regions

ANNEX 1

STANDARDS OF PERSONAL PROTECTIVE EQUIPMENT

Note: all protective clothing should conform to EN 340 : 1993 - 'Protective clothing. General requirements.'

Work activity		Protective clothing and equipment to be provided	Full title of Standard
1.	Any process or activity involving a reasonably foreseeable risk to the head from falling or moving objects.	Head protection EN 397 : 1995	Specification for industrial safety helmets.
2.	When working in areas where the circumstances involve a reasonably foreseeable risk to the head from bruising or abrasion.	Scalp protection to EN 812 : 1997	Industrial bump caps.
3.	When entering or working in a space or working with machinery or equipment where the noise level exceeds 85dB(A).	Hearing protection complying with section 10 and appendix 3 of the Code of Practice for Noise Levels in Ships published by the Department of Transport (1990):	
		EN 352-1 : 1993	Ear muffs.
		EN 352- 2 : 1993	Ear plugs.
		EN 352- 3 : 1996	Ear muffs attached to an industrial safety helmet.
		EN 458 : 1994	Hearing protectors. Recommendations for selection, use, care and maintenance.
4.	Welding and gas cutting.	Eye and face protection to EN 175 : 1997	Personal protection. Equipment for eye and face protection during welding and allied processes.
		EN 166 : 1995	Personal eye protection. Specifications.

Work activity	Protective clothing and equipment to be provided	Full title of Standard
	EN 379 : 1994	Specification for filters with switchable or dual luminous transmittance for personal eye protectors used in welding and similar operations.
	EN 169 : 1992	Specification for filters for personal eye protection equipment used in welding and similar operations.
	Body protection to EN 470-1 : 1995	Protective clothing for use in welding and allied processes. General requirements.
	Additional protection may be required in some situations (eg for particularly intense welding/cutting operations)	
Electric arc welding (in addition to above)	Safety footwear to BS 7193	Specification for lined lightweight rubber overshoes and overboots
5.	Any work activity in which there is a reasonably foreseeable risk of injury to the eye from particles, fragments or injurious substances.	Eye protection to EN 166	As above.
6.	Any work activity involving working in an atmosphere which is likely to be hazardous to health.	Note - The following items should be selected and maintained according to BS 4275 : 1997	Guide to implementing an effective respiratory protective device programme.
a)	Protection against nuisance dust mist, particles and dust of low toxicity.	Disposable dust respirators conforming to EN 149 : 1991

General purpose dust respirators conforming as appropriate to one of the following: | Specification for filtering half-masks to protect against particles. |

Work activity		Protective clothing and equipment to be provided	Full title of Standard
		EN 136 : 1998	Respiratory protective devices: Full face masks.
		EN 140 : 1998	Respiratory protective devices: Half masks and quarter masks
		EN 141 : 1990	Respiratory protective equipment: Gas filters and combined.
		EN 143 : 1990	Specification for particle filters used in respiratory protective equipment.
		EN 371 : 1992	Specification for AX gas filters and combined filters against low boiling organic compounds used in respiratory protective equipment.
		EN 372 : 1992	Specification for SX gas filters and combined filters against specific named compounds used in respiratory protective equipment.
		EN 1827: 1999	Half masks without inhalation valves, with separate filters to protect against gases or gases and particles or particles only.
b)	Protection against toxic dusts and gases of low toxicity.	Respirators conforming as appropriate to one of the following:	
		BS 7355 (EN 136)	As above.
		BS 7356 (EN 140)	As above.
		EN 141	As above.
		EN 143	As above.
		EN 371	As above.

Work activity		Protective clothing and equipment to be provided	Full title of Standard
		EN 372	As above.
		EN 405 : 1992	Valved filtering half masks for gases or gases and particles.
		Note: particulate filters may be incorporated for some applications.	
		EN 1827: 1999	Half masks without inhalation valves, with separate filters to protect against gases or gases and particles or particles only.
c)	Protection against toxic dust.	Powered dust respirators, powered dust hoods and blouses conforming as appropriate to one of the following:	
		EN 136	As above (note: this only applies to the mask).
		EN 143	As above.
		EN 12942: 1998	Specification for power assisted particle filtering devices incorporating full face masks, half masks or quarter masks.
		EN 12941: 1998	Respiratory protective devices. Specification for powered particle filtering devices incorporating helmets or hoods.

Work activity	Protective clothing and equipment to be provided	Full title of Standard
d) Protection against highly toxic atmospheres; or where there is oxygen deficiency; or as an alternative to the items above, where suitable.	Breathing apparatus conforming to: EN 1146 : 1997 (for self-rescue only) "Escape sets"	Respiratory protective devices for self rescue. Self contained open-circuit compressed air breathing apparatus incorporating a hood (compressed air apparatus with hood). Requirements, testing, marking.
	EN 137 : 1993	Specification for respiratory protective devices: self contained open-circuit compressed air breathing apparatus.
	EN 138 : 1994	Respiratory protective devices. Fresh air hose breathing apparatus for use with full face mask, half mask or mouthpiece assembly.
	EN 139 : 1994	Respiratory protective devices. Compressed air line breathing apparatus for use with a full face mask, half mask or mouthpiece assembly. Requirements, testing, marking.
	EN 269 : 1994	Respiratory protective devices. Powered fresh air hose breathing apparatus incorporating a hood.
	EN 270 : 1994	Respiratory protective devices. Compressed air line breathing apparatus incorporating a hood. Requirements, testing, marking.

Work activity	Protective clothing and equipment to be provided	Full title of Standard
	EN 271 : 1995	Respiratory protective devices: Compressed air line or powered fresh air hose breathing apparatus incorporating a hood for use in abrasive blasting operations.
	EN 402 : 1993	Respiratory protective devices for escape. Self contained open-circuit compressed air breathing apparatus with full face mask or mouthpiece assembly.
7.	Any process or activity involving working in an area where there is a reasonably foreseeable risk of injury from substances which are corrosive or likely to be absorbed through the skin.	Protective overalls, gloves or head gear, whichever is appropriate:	
	EN 340 : 1993	Protective clothing: General requirements.
	EN 465 : 1995	Protective clothing. Protection against liquid chemicals. Performance requirements for chemical protective clothing with spray-tight connections between different parts of the clothing (Type 4 equivalent).
	EN 466 : 1995	Protective clothing. Protection against liquid chemicals. Performance requirements for chemical protective clothing with liquid-tight connections between different parts of the clothing (Type 3 equivalent).

Work activity	Protective clothing and equipment to be provided	Full title of Standard
	EN 467 : 1995	Protective clothing. Protection against liquid chemicals. Performance requirements for garments providing protection to parts of the body.
8. Any process or activity involving a reasonably foreseeable risk of injury to the hands unless the use of hand protection would increase the risk.	Hand protection conforming as appropriate to :	
	EN 374	Protective gloves against chemicals and micro-organisms.
	EN 374-1 : 1994	Terminology and performance requirements.
	EN 374- 2 : 1994	Determination of resistance to penetration.
	EN 374- 3 : 1994	Determination of resistance to permeation by chemicals.
	EN 388 : 1994	Protective gloves against mechanical risks.
	EN 407 : 1994	Protective gloves against thermal risks
	EN 420 : 1994	General requirements for gloves.
	EN 511 : 1994	Protective gloves against cold.
9. Any process or activity involving particular risk of injury to the feet.	Foot protection conforming to:	
	EN 345 ; or	Safety footwear for professional use.
	EN 346, whichever is appropriate:	Protective footwear for professional use.
	EN 345- 1 : 1992	Specification.

Work activity	Protective clothing and equipment to be provided	Full title of Standard
	EN 345- 2 : 1996	Additional specifications.
	EN 346- 1 : 1992	Specification.
	EN 346-2 : 1996	Additional specifications.
	EN 347-1 : 1992	Occupational footwear for professional use.
	EN 347-2 : 1996	Additional specifications.
10. Work aloft or in any other area where there is a reasonably foreseeable risk of falling a distance of more than 2 metres.	Safety belt or harness and associated lanyard conforming to the following:	
	EN 353-1 : 1992	Specification for guided type fall arresters on a rigid anchorage line.
	EN 353- 2 : 1992	Specification for guided type fall arresters on a flexible anchorage line.
	EN 354 : 1992	Personal protective equipment against falls from a height. Lanyards.
	EN 355 : 1992	Personal protective equipment against falls from a height. Energy absorbers.
	EN 360 : 1992	Personal protective equipment against falls from a height. Retractable fall arrangements.
	EN 361 : 1992	Personal protective equipment against falls from a height. Full body harnesses.
	EN 362 : 1992	Personal protective equipment against falls from a height. Connectors.

Work activity	Protective clothing and equipment to be provided	Full title of Standard
	EN 363 : 1992	Personal protective equipment against falls from a height. Fall arrest systems.
	- or where the use of portable ladders is necessary, such ladders to be used in accordance with Chapter 15 of the Code of Safe Working Practices for Merchant Seamen (COSWP).	
11. Any work carried out from an overside position or in an exposed position where there is reasonably foreseeable risk of falling or being washed overboard or any work carried out in or from a ship's boat.	A lifebuoy with sufficient line attached ready for immediate use and either a Maritime and Coastguard Agency approved lifejacket or a lifejacket conforming as appropriate to one of the following, taking into account the area of operation:	
	EN 394 : 1994	Life jackets and personal buoyancy aids. Additional items.
	EN 396 : 1993	Life jackets and personal buoyancy aids. Life jacket 150.
	EN 399 : 1993	Life jackets and personal buoyancy aids. Life jacket 275.
	Partially inherent lifejackets must have at least 89 N of inherent buoyancy; and with the inflatable sections relying on automatic inflation.	
12. Any work activity where it is necessary to carry out repair or maintenance work on or near exposed live electrical equipment and there is a reasonably foreseeable risk of injury.	Rubber gloves conforming to: BS 697 : 1986	Specification for rubber gloves for electrical purposes *[4 classes of gloves rated at 650v and above]*

Work activity	Protective clothing and equipment to be provided	Full title of Standard
	EN 60903 : 1992	Gloves and mitts of insulating material for live working.
	Protective sleeves conforming to EN 60984 : 1993	Sleeves of insulating material for live working.
	An insulating mat (except where specially insulated flooring is installed) conforming to BS 921 : 1976	Specification. Rubber mats for electrical purposes.
	Rubber soled footwear (no standard necessary).	
	Note - gloves, sleeves and mats should protect against the appropriate voltage.	
13.	Any work activity involving a reasonably foreseeable risk of injury from vehicle movement eg during ro-ro operations.	Suitable high-visibility garment conforming to EN 471 : 1994	Specification for high-visibility warning clothing.
14.	Any work process involving exposure to heat	EN 531 : 1995	Protective clothing for industrial workers exposed to heat (excluding fire-fighters' and welders' clothing).
15.	Work in engine rooms or any area where there is a risk of fire.	Overalls made of fabric of low flammability - eg - natural fibre, high cotton content; - non-flammable clothing as appropriate	 Cotton or cotton and polyester clothing with flame-retardant finishes are available to protect against sparks and flame.